Prai

MW00988109

"The wild disconnect in the AI industry is what convinced a talented PhD working on AI problems to give up the very lucrative work for a year to write a book, and the result, called *Smart Until It's Dumb*, is the most lucid layman's account of AI and its limitations I have found."

—Andrew Orlowski, business columnist for
The Daily Telegraph

"Why did I like reading *Smart Until It's Dumb?* First, the ROI is high: Emmanuel doesn't beat around the bush or expand a 1-page blog into a 250-page book. Second, he speaks from experience. Third, he has a scientific mind, breaking down assumptions behind bold claims. Finally, he explains in layman's terms machine learning, deep learning and AI."

—Dr. Koen Pauwels, marketing professor and
principal research scientist at Amazon

"With simple language, practical examples, scientific arguments, and entertaining stories, Emmanuel presents strong evidence that, despite the noise, AI might not be ready to deliver as much as the hype suggests and it may not be anytime soon."

—Dr. Aster Santana, operations research
scientist and founder of Mip Wise

SMART UNTIL IT'S DUMB

Emmanuel Maggiori, PhD

SMART UNTIL IT'S DUMB

Why artificial intelligence
keeps making epic mistakes
(and why the AI bubble will burst)

CONTENTS

INTRODUCTION

We are in the middle of an artificial intelligence boom. Since the early 2010s, AI has made its way into our daily lives. We now use it many times a day, sometimes without even realizing it. When social networks show us personalized ads, when e-commerce websites automatically translate product reviews, when digital assistants answer our questions—all instances of AI at work. AI also operates behind the scenes, flagging fraudulent credit card transactions, optimizing mail delivery, and helping humans do our jobs in many ways.

Companies are investing astronomical sums in AI—a whopping 200 billion dollars just in the self-driving car sector. And governments, afraid of falling behind in the race, are handing out lavish grants to AI companies and research labs.

The term AI appears daily in the news, making more headlines than ever before. Sometimes, headlines announce a remarkable AI feat that may save lives; in other cases, they claim AI could take our jobs or even endanger us or cause us physical harm.

Some of the enthusiasm about AI is well deserved, as it has been widely adopted and commercially successful for the first time in history. But a lot of the hype is also just that—hype.

Have a look at the following headline, published in September 2022 by a reputed newspaper: "AI can plug the gaps in the brains of dementia sufferers." If this were true, it would be a remarkable scientific accomplishment. But when we read the article in detail, we realize that all it suggests is that AI could potentially be used somehow to improve the lives of people with dementia. The article proposed the following rather underwhelming ways to achieve that:

> The AI that helps Netflix to suggest what you'd like to watch next could anticipate what someone might be trying to say when they struggle to find the right word. Or the software behind Spotify recommendations could suggest music depending on someone's emotion or what activity they're engaged in.[1]

The business world has also been caught up in the hype. Many companies launch AI teams for fear of missing the boat, without fully knowing where or for what purpose they'll use AI. And many pretend to use AI when they don't, just to increase their chances of obtaining funding. There is also a fair amount of general confusion about what AI can and can't do. For example, an entrepreneur once told me he wanted to build an AI chatbot that acted as a psycho-therapist. But, as we'll see later on, that's probably one of the hardest things we could ask AI to do and no one has cracked that nut yet. Another entrepreneur wanted to use AI to make product recommendations and thought it would be exceedingly difficult, without realizing that it's a pretty mature and well-documented AI use case. Someone else said that fully autonomous, self-driving cars were already roaming the streets somewhere in France, even though, in reality, the vehicles he was referring to only drive back and forth on a fixed path with no traffic.

Because AI has permeated our lives and could drive profound societal changes, a lot of people are asking critical questions about it. Will AI put us in danger? Will AI take our jobs? Will AI become sentient, opening a Pandora's box of ethical dilemmas? Will self-driving cars or AI surgeons ever be released on the market, and would they be safe?

The frenzy around AI makes it very hard to answer those difficult questions because we can't tell how much of the progress in AI is real and how much of it is exaggeration or even fantasy. That's why I decided to write this book.

This book will tell you two stories. One is the story of AI—how current AI works, what it can and can't do, and what its potential dangers are. We'll discuss topics like machine learning, deep learning, and the famous AlphaGo and ChatGPT. The other story is that of the AI hype—how unreasonable expectations proliferate in the AI world. You'll hear some scandalous anecdotes from my experience working in the field—from companies building defective AI and sweeping it under the rug to researchers manipulating numbers to pretend AI works better than it does. We'll also discuss consciousness, which has recently become a hot topic after a Google employee said their AI program had become sentient—and was fired soon after.

Without further ado, I invite you to join me in unmasking the world—and craze—of artificial intelligence.

How this book is organized

The first two chapters of this book, "The Machine Learning Era" and "Deep Learning and Its Dangers," give an overview of AI in its current state. They explain how AI works and dispel some common myths about it. They also discuss the challenges and dangers of current AI methodologies. Those chapters are written in everyday language and are not intended to be an AI tutorial. If you want to become an AI practitioner, check out the suggested resources at the end of the book.

The third chapter, called "How Smart Is AI?", may be the most important one in the book. This chapter cuts through the hype by examining the things that AI can and can't do. In this chapter, we'll see why some tasks that are so easy for humans are so difficult for computers. We'll also discuss why fully autonomous cars haven't (really) been built yet and why this industry's goalposts keep moving year after year.

Chapters 4 and 5, titled "Business" and "Research" respectively, are the soap opera part of this book. These chapters tell some disturbing inside stories from my experience working in the corporate and academic AI worlds. We'll discuss how businesses spend millions on AI projects that fail in predictable ways and how academics implement, and even secretly teach to other researchers, questionable practices to inflate the apparent performance of AI. Both businesses and academics are responsible for perpetuating unreasonable expectations around AI, and we discuss them so that we can better tell hype from reality.

Finally, Chapter 6, called "The Mind," takes a philosophical turn. Recent advances in AI have reignited the topic of consciousness with questions like, "Can computers become sentient?" Advances in the field have also reignited the topic of *artificial general intelligence*—can computers do anything a human can? This chapter explores those two highly debated questions, which requires us to navigate topics like biology, philosophy, and physics. Answers here are far from simple, and opinions are divided. In the end, you'll have to pick your own lane.

Chapter 1

THE MACHINE LEARNING ERA

Google's CEO Sundar Pichai said, "AI is probably the most important thing humanity has ever worked on. I think of it as something more profound than electricity or fire."[2] And Elon Musk said that AI will be "vastly smarter than humans" before 2025.[3] (As I'm writing this in 2023, there are still a couple years left to see whether his prediction becomes true.) These two quotes illustrate a phenomenon that started in the early 2010s and has been growing ever since: society's sky-high enthusiasm about AI.

But this isn't the first time in history this has happened; there have been other AI booms in the past, none of which ended very well. Will this time be any different?

The current AI boom is centered around a methodology called *machine learning*, which is the topic of this chapter.

To help us put current events into perspective, we'll start by taking a quick tour of the previous AI booms leading up to the advent of machine learning. From there, we'll demystify machine learning in everyday terms, including seeing how machine learning works and dispelling some common myths about this methodology.

The bumpy road toward artificial intelligence

Enthusiasm about AI isn't new. The first AI boom happened during the 1960s, only a few years after electronic computers were invented. Even though computers were still very slow and had tiny memories, people could already see their potential and the hope for an all-powerful AI grew in the computer science community. In 1960, economist Herbert A. Simon famously said, "Machines will be capable, within twenty years, of doing any work that a man can do."[4] In 1963, the U.S. Department of Defense invested 2.2 million dollars in an AI research project. Some of the project's goals were to automatically translate Russian to English for intelligence operations and to create autonomous tanks for the battlefield. A few years later, the Department of Defense invested another 15 million dollars with the goal of developing computers that could understand verbal commands for hands-off operation of equipment in combat.[5] Researchers from universities and think tanks all over the world also started to promote AI and kept seeking and accepting funding for AI projects, even when the chances of their projects succeeding were slim.[6]

During this decade, researchers focused on toy problems, hoping that the techniques developed to solve these puzzles would later be applied to real-life tasks. For example, a team from MIT focused most of its AI efforts on a project to simulate a world made up of blocks and geometrical shapes. The user could manipulate the blocks and ask questions in writing, such as, "Is there a large block behind a pyramid?"

Enthusiasm was high through the '60s, but by the early '70s, it had become clear that the simple AI developed by researchers wouldn't fulfill the bigger promises that had been made; there was no success in building autonomous vehicles or useful automated translation systems, and pretty much every ambitious goal was left unattained. This led to a dramatic crash. The U.S. Defense Department cut funding for AI to almost nothing in 1974. The U.K. called for a halt to all AI research and dismantled research groups across Britain. The crash was very pronounced and led to several years of low investment and low interest in AI. This quiet period that followed the crash is now known as *the first AI winter.*

The first AI winter was grim but didn't last too long. In a bout of déjà vu, a second AI boom took place in the 1980s. This time, it was believed that a new methodology called *expert systems* would allow AI to imitate human work and thus prove itself truly useful for the first time. These systems were built by having experts write thousands of rules to convey their knowledge about a task. The rules were then put into a computer program that was meant to imitate their expert work.

The AI enthusiasm of this period reached monumental proportions. Notably, the Japanese government spent the equivalent of 400 million U.S. dollars on a research project promising that "computers would be able to converse with humans in natural language and understand speech and pictures."[7] In the U.S., the Department of Defense launched a project promising remarkable advances in AI, including the development of an autonomous vehicle and an AI assistant for aircraft pilots. They spent a whopping sum of one billion dollars on these endeavors.

This time, enthusiasm for AI also spread to the private sector. Most large companies at the time, such as Xerox and Texas Instruments, started their own in-house AI teams. The computer giant DEC (later acquired by Compaq) grew its AI team to 700 employees.[8]

But the principles behind this AI boom, such as writing thousands of rules by hand, soon proved impractical and ineffective. So, by the end of the '80s, enthusiasm started to wane, as promises once again went unfulfilled. The Japanese project, for example, failed to imitate natural human speech and was terminated in 1992. Its U.S. counterpart also failed to make the intended advances and was terminated the same year. Start-ups in the AI field started to lose millions of dollars every year because, ironically, growing and maintaining their AI systems required a large amount of manual work. The most cutting-edge AI companies at the time, such as Symbolics and Lisp Machine, filed for bankruptcy and thousands of people lost their jobs.[9] A new period of stagnation ensued, called *the second AI winter.*

The two unfortunate periods of unfulfilled AI hype, and their subsequent winters, created a stigma around AI that haunted the field for a long time. Many AI researchers even started calling their work by a different name, such as "cognitive systems," to avoid the negativity associated with the words "artificial intelligence."

In the decades that followed, research into AI continued at a more moderate pace and interesting advances were made, many of them facilitated by the much faster computers that were becoming available. The most remarkable milestone was in 1997, when a computer beat the world chess champion Garry Kasparov. This computer, called Deep Blue, internally simulated 200 million game moves per second to assess their value and select the most promising move to play on each turn.

Throughout this period, AI research was carried out in a more cautious and less extravagant way compared to the craze of the '60s and '80s.

Then the 2010s arrived.

The machine learning revolution

Since the early 2010s, there's been a new AI boom that sur-
passes the previous two by far. This time, the enthusiasm is
around *machine learning,* a methodology in which computers
automatically learn things by scanning massive amounts of
data. With the advent of the internet, more and more data
became available, and technological advances made storing
and processing data cheaper and faster than ever. This made
machine learning possible at scale for the first time.

As opposed to the two previous AI booms, this time
AI—in the form of machine learning—has been widely
adopted and used in many successful commercial applications. In fact, you probably interact with machine learning
software several times a day. For instance, when an online
store recommends a product to you, a computer has analyzed your past actions to learn what may interest you. Or, if
you type "inglorious bastards" into Google's search bar, the
search engine suggests, "Did you mean *inglourious basterds*?"
even though neither "inglourious" nor "basterds" is a word in
the English dictionary. (Both parts of the movie title were
deliberately misspelled.) Google's machines automatically
scanned a large body of text (newspapers, blogs, Wikipedia
articles, past searches, and so on) to pick up those words'
most common spellings.

Machine learning has also dramatically improved performance at tasks that computer scientists struggled with for

years, including recognizing objects in images and beating human players at the infamously tricky game of Go. These milestones—which some people thought were decades away—were highly publicized and drove significant attention to machine learning.

The thing is, with machine learning's successes also came a lot of frenzy and hype. For example, a company that is regarded as an "AI start-up" seems to attract 15% to 50% more funding than other types of tech start-ups,[10] so companies overuse the word "AI" to garner investors' attention. Some of them have been caught red-handed pretending to use AI when, in reality, they were using human workers to do the alleged AI work.[11] Notably, the CEO of a start-up was charged with fraud in 2020 for pretending to develop AI software that could interpret video reviews posted by customers, when it appears that workers in India were being paid to watch the videos and register their impressions.[12] A venture capital firm studied 2,830 start-ups in Europe that were classified as AI companies and found that 40% of them weren't using AI in a way that was material to the business.[13]

Just like in the previous two AI booms of the '60s and '80s, autonomous vehicles are one of the most important promises being put on the table. The industry of autonomous cars has grown to an unprecedented size, bringing in more than 200 billion dollars of investment over the past few years.[14] And, of course, there's Tesla, one of the highest valued companies in the world, which has promised several times to develop a fully autonomous car. Later on, we'll talk more about this industry and whether its promises are likely to be fulfilled.

Also, speculative scenarios have started to flood the news. We're often told that AI will endanger our livelihoods or even our lives, or that we must control AI and align it to human values or else our civilization could crumble. And to make things even more puzzling, in 2022, the news went viral that a Google employee had claimed that Google's AI chatbot had become sentient.[15]

With such an odd mixture of practical successes and outlandish claims, it is hard to separate the wheat from the chaff. Will computers beat humans at every task? Will computers become conscious? Will robots replace human workers? The world has already paid twice in dramatic crashes for excessive enthusiasm around AI—will this time be any different? The sentiment seems to be that this time is "the one," but that was the case in the two previous AI booms as well. No one can tell the future, but the best guide to navigating the chaos is to understand how machine learning works.

How machine learning works

Suppose an innovative start-up wants to build a humanoid robot that "walks" around the city, surrounded by other pedestrians and traffic. The start-up is looking to write the software that decides whether the robot should cross the road or wait.

If you've ever crossed a road, you're certainly familiar with the thought process we humans go through in that split second; we tend to ask ourselves a series of questions. These questions can usually be reduced to "if" analyses: "If there are no cars on the street, cross over." "If the closest car is far away and driving slowly, cross over." "If the pedestrian crosswalk signal is red, wait."

To program the robot, the first idea that comes to mind is to manually write a computer program that imitates the decision process we go through when crossing roads. This is very easy to do because computer programming is performed by writing down easy-to-read logic and instructions in text files.

Have a look at the following hypothetical computer program for road crossing:

"If distance to closest car on road < 100 feet, then wait; otherwise, if speed of closest car on road < 20 mph, then cross over; otherwise, wait."

This snippet of program code imitates our mental pondering. If you read it carefully, you'll see it's probably quite similar to what you actually think about in a split second before crossing the road. The program takes two inputs, possibly captured with a camera or a radar: the distance to the closest car on the road and the speed of the closest car. The inputs are combined through a series of "if-otherwise" conditions that mimic our train of thought. As the program runs, the conditions are evaluated (for instance, "Is the distance to the closest car below 100 feet?") and verdicts are reached (either "cross over" or "wait").

Back in the 1980s, the AI community thought that the process of writing down thousands of rules manually would be a sure way to build truly intelligent machines. So, domain experts were hired to try to distill their thought processes into numerous rules. This idea, called *expert systems,* drove the AI hype in the '80s.

One of the big issues with this approach was that it was very difficult and impractical—teaching a machine to perform any task required *a lot* of rules. Also, experts had a hard time describing their intuitive reasoning as a set of inflexible, robotic rules, and different experts often disagreed. Coming up with rules was also rather arbitrary, based on subject hunches more than statistical evidence (should the robot cross the road when the closest car is 1,000 or 2,000 feet away?).

Many years later, machine learning came to the rescue. This methodology overcomes the limitations of writing rules by hand one by one. To understand machine learning, we just need a tiny change of mindset. Let's have a look again at our road-crossing software code:

"If distance to closest car on road < 100 feet, then wait; otherwise, if speed of closest car on road < 20 mph, then cross over; otherwise, wait."

Now, just rethink the program as follows:

"If <u>some input</u> < <u>some number</u>, then <u>some recommendation</u>; otherwise, if <u>some input</u> < <u>some number</u>, then <u>some recommendation</u>; otherwise, <u>some recommendation</u>."

This is a *template* of the program, rather than the program itself, because it contains *blanks* (here represented by the underlined words) that must be filled in. The idea behind machine learning is that, instead of manually writing every detail of the computer program, the practitioner decides its general shape (the template) and lets the computer automatically fill in the blanks in a useful way. So, the general structure of the program is given, and the details are filled in automatically.

But how can the computer "know" whether a blank should be filled with "20 mph" or "50 mph" for the rule to be useful for the task? Or how does it know whether the input field "speed of closest car" is useful at all for making road-crossing decisions? Enter data.

Suppose the Ministry of Transport has spent so observing pedestrians crossing the road and re outcome: *dead* or *alive*. (Forgive me this rather dramatic example, but it will help us understand the role of data in machine learning.) Let's imagine the Ministry of Transport has collected the following data:

Distance to closest car (ft)	Speed of closest car (mph)	Outcome
900	20	Alive
1000	45	Alive
300	7	Alive
20	20	Dead
100	30	Dead
100	10	Alive
500	30	Alive

In machine learning jargon, this is called a *dataset*. Each row represents one pedestrian and contains both the context at the time of road crossing (distance to and speed of closest car) and the outcome after they crossed the street. In a realistic scenario, we'd have thousands of rows instead of just seven, and many more columns to describe the context instead of just the distance and speed of the closest car, but you get the gist.

Now, the computer uses this data to figure out how to fill in the blanks in the template in an effective way. This is typically done by automatically simulating many "If some input < some number" decisions in a manner of guess and heck. The computer fills in the blanks with many possible combinations of values then checks whether the resulting rule is effective on the dataset according to some criterion given by the user (in this case, "try to make dead pedestrians wait while make alive pedestrians cross over"). For instance, the rule "If distance to closest car < 150 ft, then wait" would have saved the lives of the two dead pedestrians in the above dataset, so it would be deemed a good rule. By trying many input/number/recommendation combinations in a systematic way, the computer identifies the most promising ones and fills in the blanks in the template with them. This is called *training* or *learning*.

Note that, in machine learning, a computer program fills in the details of another computer program. To avoid confusion, the program created by machine learning—the one whose blanks are filled in—is often called the *model*. If you ever work with machine learning practitioners, you'll hear them constantly speak of building models instead of writing programs.

That's it. If you've followed along this far, you know the gist of how current machine learning works. The job of a machine learning practitioner—or *data scientist*—is to choose what template to use and then run a program that automatically scans datasets to fill in the blanks.

One of the most commonly used templates nowadays is the one we just saw, which consists of several "If some input < some value" decisions. The computer has no freedom to do anything other than fill in the blanks in that simple template, and it cannot escape the structure of the decisions (for instance, switching the "<" to a ">" or a "≠").

The more advanced machine learning techniques are no different in principle; they are just variations of this method. For example, a technique known as *random forest* has become the bread and butter of machine learning (in fact, it comes up in most job interviews for data science positions). This method also uses templates with "If <u>some input</u> < <u>some value</u>" rules, except that, instead of just creating one program, the data scientist creates several different programs for the same task and averages their outputs. This proves more robust than just creating a single program and trusting its results. Even though it may require some skill to make all this work in practice, current machine learning is exceedingly simple *in principle*. Even the methodologies behind deep learning, which we'll discuss later, follow the fill-in-the-blank recipe.

Why machine learning is so successful

A couple of years ago, I worked as a consultant for a company that was using software to automatically identify relevant products and recommend them to existing clients. The program code contained 10,000 lines of text that consisted of a long list of rules, all written by hand ("If the client purchased product X, then recommend product Y"). Due to its sheer size and complexity, the program had become really hard to manage. In fact, the external consulting company that had built the software kept charging the wages of four full-time engineers to update and maintain the huge program.

Our task was to replace this cumbersome program with one built with machine learning. We had access to a large historical dataset including clients' past purchases. After working for only a few days, we built a machine learning program to make product recommendations based on the data, and it consistently beat the old program with its manually written rules—generated at a fraction of the effort.

Compared to writing rules by hand one by one, machine learning lets us create lengthy programs that contain many rules without much human effort. And thanks to data, the rules are added in an evidence-driven way, which makes them highly useful. Sometimes, machine learning even stumbles upon useful rules that humans overlook. For instance, the computer may identify that people who like a certain product tend to also like another totally unrelated product, or it may identify a factor that we hadn't thought about to help us cross roads safely.

All of these advantages combined have made machine learning a powerful tool, and it has changed the way we approach writing software—nowadays, most people wouldn't even consider writing tens of thousands of rules one by one to recommend products to clients or correct spelling mistakes.

Now that we've established why machine learning is great, the time has come to dispel some myths about it.

Can computers learn by themselves?

While machine learning has become increasingly popular, so have some speculations around it. One of them is that computers can somehow "learn by themselves" and even go rogue. In 2014, for instance, Elon Musk suggested that if a computer learns how to filter spam, it could conclude that "the best way of getting rid of spam email is getting rid of humans."[16] In 2017, DeepMind—Google's AI subsidiary—announced that they'd managed to make a computer learn how to play games "without human knowledge" involved in the process.[17] Since then, many people have asked me whether it's true that now you can "just tell a computer what you want and it learns how to do it."

You've probably noticed from our previous explanation of machine learning that the whole process seems horribly restrictive. Why use such simple templates, like "If <u>some input</u> < <u>some number</u>"? Can't we let the computer learn more stuff, with more sophisticated rules? That would let it learn "anything it wants" and thus become smarter, wouldn't it?

It is tempting to think that with a more flexible template, the computer would be able to learn more interesting and expressive stuff. We could, for instance, extend the template to multiply pairs of inputs ("If <u>some input</u> × <u>some other input</u> < <u>some number</u>"). This would allow more complicated rules like "If distance to closest car × speed of closest car < 500." We could make the template even more expressive by allowing it to multiply (or divide) sets of three numbers, and so on. We could even turn "<" into a blank, so that the computer can fill it in with different operators, like "=," "≠," and "≤." In the most extreme case, we could have no template at all and let the computer combine characters freely to write *any* possible computer program. Sounds like a dream! But is it?

Consider the following statistic: Between 2001 and 2009, the yearly consumption of cheese in the U.S. was highly correlated with the number of people who died by becoming entangled in their bed sheets.[18] This is a fact; the numbers prove it. However, the phenomena are probably not causally related—it was just a coincidence. But if we only trust the numbers, we may be led to believe that cheese consumption and bed sheet strangulation are related phenomena. In fact, if we search long enough for correlations in all sorts of phenomena, we'll surely find phenomena that are highly correlated just by chance.

In machine learning, if we use a very flexible template that can be filled in in too many possible ways, then the computer is prone to stumbling upon spurious correlations and building rules based on them. The data "proves" that these rules are useful but, in reality, their apparent usefulness is just a coincidence in the data.

Imagine for a minute that our road-crossing data included more information about each pedestrian, such as their phone number, height, and weight, and that we used a template that allowed us to multiply inputs together. Now, suppose the computer tries out the rule "If phone number × height < 300,000, cross over; otherwise wait" and the data proves that this rule would have told the survivors to cross over and the dead ones to wait. That looks like an effective rule, so the computer incorporates the rule into the road-crossing program.

But any logical human can see that the effectiveness of that rule must be just a coincidence—why would the phone number, let alone the phone number multiplied by the height, have anything to do with survival rates of road crossing? The rule is quite obviously meaningless. But the computer does not know that. It does not "understand" what the phone number or the height are. To the eyes of the computer filling in the blanks, if a rule proves useful as measured on the dataset, then it is a good rule. Period. So, if the template is very free, instead of creating a smarter program for the task at hand, it ends up generating a dumber one due to the addition of nonsensical rules. Those rules are ineffective when the program is used later on, as the coincidental correlation will likely disappear.

To avoid adding nonsensical rules, we must limit the set of things the computer can learn from the data—we must help the computer learn. So, data scientists constantly rely on human knowledge—or *assumptions*—about the task to restrict the computer's freedom to learn and point it in the right direction.

For example, a good data scientist would decide *not* to include the phone number at all as part of the possible inputs, so that the computer didn't even have the chance to use it in a rule. A good data scientist would also choose a template that seems appropriate for the task. While rules of the type "If <u>some input</u> < <u>some number</u>" are very popular because they mimic our train of thought, other choices may be more appropriate depending on the task.

Let's take a look at how data scientists deal with non-numerical inputs, since it illustrates very well how assumptions are used. Suppose that a column in the dataset describes the size of an oncoming vehicle as a category, such as "Compact," "Minivan," "Van" and "Truck." In this particular case, the data scientist will map the categories to numbers (say, 1, 2, 3 and 4), where larger numbers represent larger vehicles. This enables the model to easily create rules that distinguish small vehicles from large ones ("If size < 3").

Now, consider a column with the car manufacturer—"Ford," "Fiat," "Renault," and so on. A sensible data scientist would *not* map those categories to consecutive numbers because the brands are not an ordered quantity like the size of a vehicle. Doing such mapping would allow the blank-filling program to build strange rules like "If car brand < 5." The decision of not mapping brand names to numbers is based on the data scientist's understanding of car sizes and brands and not something the computer discovers on its own.

So, if you snoop into the daily life of a data scientist, you'll see that the bulk of the job involves building a tailor-made machine learning solution for the task at hand, leveraging prior knowledge and assumptions to help the machine learn. Machine learning is not carried out by giving all the data we have to the machine and letting it learn anything it wants. As we've seen, giving the computer that much freedom would be highly ineffective for building useful software. As we'll discuss later on, this holds true even with the most advanced AI built to date.

There is a variant of machine learning called *reinforcement learning,* where the computer builds its own dataset by trying different actions at random and measuring their outcomes. For instance, we could send a physical robot to roam the streets and do stuff—even stupid stuff like jumping into traffic—to collect a valuable dataset to learn from. One of the most familiar applications of this is in online advertising, where users are shown different ads at random to track which ones they click on and which ones they ignore. Afterward, machine learning tries to learn users' preferences from that data.

This idea of computers trying actions is often a source of fear in AI. That's what Elon Musk probably had in mind—that a spam filter allowed to take random actions would find evidence that killing people reduces spam.

However, reinforcement learning doesn't escape the need

for the computer's actions to be governed by human assumptions. The data scientist must explicitly program which actions the machine is allowed to try out. In the case of spam, for instance, a possible action could be "Flag emails as spam if they contain the words 'free' and 'Viagra'." After trying out the action, we'd keep track of how many users reported receiving fewer spam emails. This data would then be used to find associations between actions and reduction of spam.

If the data scientist allows the computer to try outlandish actions, say, "send a rocket to the moon," it is unlikely that an action will ever be found that has an impact on spam—or the actions that are found to be effective are spurious correlations. If the data scientist allowed *any* action by letting the computer write random program code, it is unlikely that the computer would ever generate a piece of code that does something useful. So, the data scientist must rely on assumptions about the task to direct the computer to focus only on a handful of promising actions. Even if a data scientist was careless and allowed out-of-scope actions, these actions would still have to be programed into the system.

In the book *Human Compatible*, Stuart Russell gives several predictions about AI. One of them is that AI could learn to disable its "off-switch" and thus become uncontrollable. He tells us, "Suppose a machine has the objective of fetching the coffee. If it is sufficiently intelligent, it will certainly understand that it will fail in its objective if it is switched off before completing its mission. Thus, the objective of fetching coffee creates, as a necessary subgoal, the objective of disabling the off-switch."[19]

However, within current machine learning, this isn't a real concern—why would anyone include the action "disable the off-switch" as part of the available actions to try out for coffee delivery? Even if the action was allowed, the stars would have to align for the computer to ever try out that action and measure a significant positive impact in the efficiency of coffee delivery.

General or narrow?

Machine learning operates in so many facets of our lives that it might seem like we can build one program and use it for many things, but the reality is that each task is narrowly defined and its solution tailor-made. Think of your daily visit to an online store. You're shown a personalized list of recommended products on the homepage. This is powered by machine learning—the computer learns to identify appealing products from your past product purchases and ratings and those of other users. You then search for a product and you're shown a list of candidate products sorted by relevance. Machine learning is used to sort the results by relevance—the computer scans a dataset of which products have been shown to users in the past and which ones have been clicked on or ignored. Now you visit a product page and read some user reviews, some of which are translated from another language.

This, too, uses machine learning, specifically a program that learned how to translate sentences from studying a dataset of documents written in multiple languages.

But it's important to remark that there isn't one piece of software that serves all those tasks. Instead, machine learning is *narrow*—each task is tackled separately with its own model, assumptions and data.

The data conundrum

What makes machine learning powerful is the use of specialized data for each task, so acquiring the right data is very important. But data acquisition can be one of the most challenging aspects of the machine learning process.

The most common type of machine learning, known as *supervised learning,* requires the data to be *labeled,* meaning that each sample must be tagged with the correct answer. For instance, in the road-crossing scenario, each data point was labeled "alive" or "dead" based on the pedestrian's outcome. Or, for example, in the case of automated translation, the dataset used for learning typically contains millions of sentences in one language paired with correct translations into another language. This way, the machine identifies useful rules to associate words in one language to words in the other language ("If 'Good morning', output 'Buenos días'"). So, in most cases, machine learning needs a long list of correct answers to learn a task effectively—like studying for an exam by reading lots of previous exam questions marked with their correct answers.

Sometimes, obtaining labeled data can be hard work. In fact, the data may have to be manually labeled by humans. That's often the case, for instance, with automatic image categorization. A famous dataset for that task, called ImageNet, contains 14 million images, all labeled by hand—one by one—into categories like "strawberry" or "airplane."

If you're working on a niche application domain—say, classifying crops on satellite images or detecting conditions in medical images—a publicly available dataset like ImageNet won't do the job; you'll need your own set of images specific to your problem, which should be labeled into your own categories. A friend of mine, with the help of a coworker, had to manually label 200,000 images in order to use machine learning for image categorization in a niche domain. (I heard it wasn't fun.)

Since data labeling is rather challenging, some companies are offering it as a service. For instance, I received this message on LinkedIn a few days ago:

"Hello Emmanuel. I'm offering data annotation by teams located in [country known for its low-cost workforce]. Are you interested?"

In some cases, if you're fortunate enough, you may be able to collect labels generated by someone else instead of hand labeling them one by one yourself. For instance, in targeted advertising, you can keep a record of your users' clicks on ads to label them as "relevant" or "irrelevant." And in translation, you may find a lot of phrases written in multiple languages by gathering public documents from the European Union.

If you're really lucky, you may even be able to produce the labels automatically. Suppose your task is to predict the next word in a piece of text, as Gmail does when you're writing an email. To complete this task with machine learning, each row of your dataset must contain the beginning of a phrase labeled with its correct next word, such as "I forgot to include the..." labeled with "attachment." Here's a trick: An enormous dataset for this task can be easily produced by collecting phrases from existing emails and turning the last word from each sentence into a label (so, we convert "I forgot the attachment" into "I forgot the..." labeled with "attachment"). This strategy is called *self-supervised learning* because the labels are generated automatically from the data. While this idea is very useful, it can only be applied in very limited scenarios—when we want to predict a hidden part of the data from the remaining, unhidden part. With other machine learning tasks, we're rarely so lucky.

Self-supervised learning was used to train GPT-3, a famous model capable of generating convincing text from an initial prompt. Its training labels were created by hiding the last bit of text from existing sentences, just like explained above. Since GPT-3 was trained to guess only the next word or so, longer text is generated by repeatedly feeding it its own outputs. But self-supervised learning wasn't enough to take

GPT-3 to the next level. Its successor, ChatGPT, is a model especially designed to excel at conversation, but this required supervised learning—humans were asked to manually label thousands of input phrases with their expected answers and also rank different answers by quality, and this data was fed into the model to refine it.

There is also a type of machine learning, known as *unsupervised learning*, that doesn't require the data to be labeled. While it may sound like an upgrade, in reality it's simply used to tackle different tasks from those of supervised and self-supervised learning. In general, it is used to analyze the structure of the data. For instance, it may be used to group together users with similar interests or to reduce the number of columns in a dataset while avoiding the loss of too much information. So, while unsupervised learning is useful within its scope, it doesn't eliminate the need for labels.

In most cases, labeled data is still required, and it can be quite laborious to obtain!

Case study: Detection of hate speech

Machine learning is as good as the data it learns from. So, it is important to be careful when collecting and labeling the data, especially when the application is highly sensitive. But is this always how people do it?

Consider the case of using machine learning to automatically detect hate speech in written text like online comments.

As usual, you require a dataset with sample sentences paired with their correct labels—"hate speech" or "not hate speech." But who is in charge of judging and labeling the sample sentences? And what criteria will they use to do so? Note that, after it learns, the machine will end up mirroring the way humans labeled the sentences in the dataset.

Let's have a look at how a group of researchers from Cornell University tackled this task, as explained in one of their scientific articles.[20] First, they downloaded a list of words identified by internet users as hate speech from a website called Hatebase.org. This website is crowdsourced, so any user can contribute by adding words. Some of the words currently on the list are "bird," "monkey" and "Pepsi."

Afterward, the Cornell researchers picked a sample of Twitter users who had, at some point, used a word from that list. From those users, they then randomly selected 25,000 tweets.

The researchers then sent the 25,000 tweets to an outsourced data-labeling company to have human workers read them and label them one by one. They explained the process as follows:

> Workers were asked to label each tweet as one of three categories: hate speech, offensive but not hate speech, or neither offensive nor hate speech. They were provided with our definition along with a paragraph explaining it in further detail.

Each tweet was labeled by three different people and the majority label was chosen. However, if the three workers all disagreed on the label, the tweet was removed from the dataset entirely.

This process raises eyebrows. Why restrict the data to a subset of users already deemed hateful? This creates a dataset with a disproportionate number of hateful tweets compared to the general population, possibly encouraging the machine to over-detect hate speech. Even then, why use an ambiguous list of words from Hatebase.org to do so, which doesn't even follow the researchers' own definition of hate speech? Also, how can they make sure that outsourced workers understand and follow their instructions correctly? And how can they justify outright eliminating samples on which the workers didn't agree?

Cornell continued their research on hate speech and, two years later, announced a worrying finding: Tweets written by African Americans are flagged as hate speech more often than those written by people of other backgrounds.[21] But let's see how they came to this conclusion.

The thing is, it's not possible to know which tweets are flagged as hate speech, as this information isn't shared by Twitter. So, instead, the researchers used machine learning to identify tweets likely to be deemed hate speech from a large database of tweets. One of the machine learning models for this task was built using the dataset of 25,000 tweets mentioned above.

The remaining task was to know whether the analyzed tweets were written by black or non-black people. They also used machine learning for this. But it can be difficult to determine a Twitter user's skin color. So, they created a dataset of tweets labeled as "black aligned" and "white aligned" based on whether "they contained language associated with either of those demographics." For example, if a tweet contained a word considered to be uttered usually by white people, it was labeled as "white aligned."

The researchers from Cornell acknowledged that the resulting model "couldn't conclusively predict the race of a tweet's author," but they used it anyway for the remainder of their research. After analyzing many tweets, they found out that those deemed as hate speech by one machine learning model were more likely to also be deemed as "black aligned" by their other machine learning model. The researchers concluded, "We found consistent, systematic and substantial racial biases."

There may be something to this conclusion, but is it really proven by this research? The data was obtained in such a muddled way, so how can we trust the machine learning models that used it to draw conclusions?

This example illustrates that even people from reputed institutions aren't immune to poor handling of data. As often said in the data community, "Garbage in, garbage out."

Chapter 2

DEEP LEARNING AND ITS DANGERS

Some tasks, such as image categorization or speech recognition, are especially difficult for computers to handle. For many years, researchers struggled to make progress in them. But then the *deep learning* revolution happened.

Deep learning is a type of machine learning that has made many headlines. Its first remarkable milestone was in 2012, during a popular competition for image categorization. A deep learning approach won the competition, attaining a performance far higher than other approaches.[22] Its creators used 1.2 million images to train the model, manually labeled into 1,000 different categories.

In another remarkable milestone, in 2015, the company DeepMind released AlphaGo, a computer program capable of beating human players at the infamous game of *Go*. This board game has more legal positions than the number of atoms in the universe, so a lot of people thought the task was impossible. AlphaGo proved them wrong. This event gained widespread public attention for deep learning.

Since then, deep learning has become the go-to methodology for a number of complicated problems, including image and video analysis and natural language processing. It is also the methodology behind the fancy AI that generates fake images or makes any picture look like a Van Gogh painting, and it also powers the popular ChatGPT chatbot.

But the astounding progress in deep learning also led to a lot of speculation and mysticism around it. For example, a lot of people have compared deep learning with the structure of the human brain. Others have claimed that it can learn without human input. Some have been led to believe that deep learning doesn't require labeled data at all—someone recently asked me whether it was true that computers can now create their own simulated artificial worlds and learn from them.

More importantly, some people have pointed out that deep learning could be dangerous. And researchers have even gone to great lengths to prove how we can trick deep learning into giving unexpected outputs.

In this chapter, we'll see why some tasks are extra hard for computers and how deep learning tackles them. We'll then dispel some common myths about deep learning. Finally, we'll take a look into the dangers of deep learning, which should not be taken lightly.

Why some tasks are extra hard

Consider the task of image categorization, where a computer program must automatically determine what category of object an image contains.

When we humans look at an image, we intuitively "see" meaningful objects in it. But the way images are represented and stored in computers (or even our retinas) is quite difficult to analyze.

In a computer, an image is represented by a table of numbers. Each number—known as a *pixel*—describes the intensity of light at a precise location. These numbers typically go from 0 (black) to 255 (white). The following is a toy example of an image of a bright spot over a black background:

And now let's see its corresponding digital representation:

0	0	0	0	0	0	0	0	0	0	0
0	0	0	0	0	0	0	0	0	0	0
0	0	0	0	170	255	170	0	0	0	0
0	0	0	255	255	255	255	255	0	0	0
0	0	170	255	255	255	255	255	170	0	0
0	0	255	255	255	255	255	255	255	0	0
0	0	170	255	255	255	255	255	170	0	0
0	0	0	0	170	255	170	0	0	0	0
0	0	0	0	0	0	0	0	0	0	0
0	0	0	0	0	0	0	0	0	0	0

In general, images have many more pixels per square inch than what you see above, so we don't see the image as pixelated and blurry. My smartphone, for instance, draws over 200,000 pixels per square inch of screen. In case you're wondering, color images consist of three tables, one for each primary color—red, green and blue.

In the previous chapter, we saw that templates of the type "If some input < some number" are commonly used in machine learning. But in the examples of that chapter, the inputs in isolation were very easy to interpret and highly useful for the task, such as "distance to closest car."

But with images, the situation is much more complicated. Each pixel in isolation doesn't give us useful information about the content of the image. For instance, knowing that the pixel at row 3 and column 5 takes the value 170 is of very little use for interpreting the image.

Also, a certain object—say, a cat—can appear in many different ways. Cats come in all shapes and colors and may be located in different areas of the image. Even black or white cats aren't uniformly black or white, due to lighting conditions, shadows, glow, and any number of other factors.

So, if we want to interpret the content of an image, we have to analyze many pixels at the same time in a complex way.

The usual templates from "traditional" machine learning, such as "If <u>some input</u> < <u>some number</u>," work well if the inputs are already known to be quite useful ("distance to closest car" is for sure related to the pedestrian's outcome). Otherwise, the learning program struggles to find useful rules. Traditional templates are effective in simple image analysis tasks, such as identifying digits from 0 to 9 in tiny images, but they perform poorly at more complicated tasks.

Most tasks that involve analyzing raw data, like speech or written text, are equally challenging and great candidates for deep learning. For example, speech audio is represented as a sequence of numbers describing air pressure—which is far from telling us which words are uttered. And written text is stored as a sequence of numbers that represent letters, which is also quite far from a useful representation we can use to extract meaning.

So, in those cases, we have to dig deeper.

How deep learning works

You've probably applied a *filter* to an image before, maybe on Instagram or Photoshop. Filters are commonly used to make images look better, for example, by making certain colors look brighter or adding a sepia effect.

Filters can also be used to highlight patterns in an image. For instance, there's a type of filter that highlights object boundaries by detecting areas with sharp color changes. The resulting image is bright in areas near boundaries and dark elsewhere. You can try it for yourself on Photoshop (just click on Filter → Stylize → Find edges).

Basic filters can only highlight the presence of basic features like boundaries, lines or areas of a specific color (think green screen); they cannot detect high-level objects like cats. But the inventors of deep learning had the clever idea to detect higher-level objects using combinations of basic filters.

Suppose you first apply a handful of filters directly to the input image to highlight some basic patterns, such as lines in different locations or angles. You then combine the resulting filtered images to produce a new image. This new image doesn't look like the original one anymore, but it contains interesting low-level information, such as the location of lines.

Afterward, you apply a second set of filters to this new image. While these filters are also quite basic, they are applied to an image that was already filtered into a series of individual lines and is therefore easier for the computer to parse. So, they can be configured to highlight slightly more complicated things, such as parallel lines.

You continue applying basic filters, combining the results, and then applying more filters on top. After many steps, you could use this system to highlight entire objects like cats. This sequence of filters detects progressively more complicated shapes, for instance: dark lines → parallel dark lines → whiskers → faces → cats.

So, a base assumption underlying deep learning is that the objects of interest can be represented hierarchically and thus detected through the repeated application of filters. For instance, in deep learning, a cat is detected by the presence of its parts, for instance a face and a tail, each of which is also detected by the presence of its parts—whiskers, eyes, fur, etc. And each of these features is also detected by the presence of its parts—parallel dark lines, pupils, hair, etc.—and so on and so forth.

The challenge to all this is that coming up with the right sequence of filters is really tedious, if not impossible. Imagine trying to come up with filters to detect cats of all possible shapes and colors and that could be curled up in strange positions or up in a tree or partially occluded by some other object in the scene.

Enter machine learning.

In deep learning, data scientists design a model template with an exact description of how many filters should be applied and how they should be organized. For example, the template may contain 16 successive filtering steps with 32 different filters in each step.

Also, the data scientist includes other useful operations

in the template besides filtering. For example, the image is typically shrunk—reducing its number of pixels—right after every filtering step. So, the image becomes smaller and smaller as it passes through the filters. This makes the image lose its fine details. While this may sound like a loss, in reality it's really helpful because, in general, we don't care about the exact location of high-level objects like furry tails to identify cats—we just need to know that there's a furry tail somewhere in the image.

Overall, this model looks like a funnel: an image enters the funnel and is progressively filtered and shrunk. The final output is a tiny image that is bright if a cat (or whatever object you're looking for) is detected and dark if it is not detected. This funnel is known as a *convolutional neural network,* or CNN, and has become the bread and butter of deep learning for image categorization.

But, while the general template is designed by hand by the data scientist, no one decides in advance what each filter should do. So, the template looks like this:

"Apply filters $\underline{X}$, $\underline{Y}$ and $\underline{Z}$ to the image and combine the results, then shrink the image to half its size, then apply filters $\underline{R}$, $\underline{S}$ and $\underline{T}$ and combine the results, then shrink the image to half its size, then apply filters $\underline{U}$, $\underline{V}$ and $\underline{W}$, ..."

Machine learning is then used to fill in the blanks in the template (the underlined letters above). For this, the machine must try out a multitude of combinations of different filters and measure how good they are at the task by comparing against the labeled training dataset.

The training process starts with a completely random set of filters, so the initial model is generally useless. Afterward, it starts altering the filters progressively to find promising improvements. This is akin to an appointment with the eye doctor who tries out several glasses' prescriptions, changing them little by little until finding the one you're most comfortable with. But the process is much lengthier and more chaotic.

This search for a good combination of filters can take hours or even days. The availability of powerful graphics cards for this task since the early 2010s has significantly accelerated the process. With a bit of luck and a lot of computation, the resulting CNN model is highly effective at categorizing images. Modified versions of this CNN approach have also been used for many popular fun applications, including generating fake images or transferring the style of one image onto another.

Deep learning beyond images

The template used for image categorization—the CNN—can be used and adapted for other tasks as well, provided that the assumptions behind that template hold true.

For example, the task of detecting the presence of a word in a voice recording is quite similar to detecting whether there is a cat in an image, as a word can be detected by the presence of its individual sounds. The main difference is that an image is a 2-D thing (a table of numbers) while audio is a 1-D thing (a string of numbers indicating air pressure through time). The same concept of CNNs can be easily used for this task, except that the filtering and shrinking operations are performed over the 1-D audio signal instead of the 2-D image.

But CNNs cannot be effectively applied to all problems. Consider the case of analyzing written text, as in the task of machine translation. Text is represented in an even more obscure way than images. For instance, the lowercase character "a" is represented in a computer by the number 97, while an uppercase "A" is represented by the number 65. This is completely arbitrary (at least with images, the numbers represent a physical thing—the brightness). So, applying CNNs to these numbers is ineffective.

Instead, the text is first processed word by word using a machine learning model that replaces each word with a set of numbers that try to convey its topic. This transformation is designed to replace related words with numbers that are close to each other and unrelated words with numbers that are far apart from each other. For example, "Paris" and "France" are replaced with close-by numbers, whereas the numbers for "Paris" and "Penguin" are far apart. The model learns to map words to close-by numbers by scanning thousands of documents and identifying which words are likely to co-occur.

Processing the initial input text in this way might make it less meaningful to the human eye, but it makes it much easier for a computer to analyze.

Then the processed input—now a string of sets of numbers—is passed on to a second machine learning model especially built to analyze text and trained with its own dedicated dataset. Instead of a CNN, a different kind of model called *long short-term memory,* or LSTM, is usually used for this task. This type of model is better adapted to analyzing sequences of data because it processes one word (represented by a number set) at a time instead of trying to tackle an entire sentence in one go. When the LSTM processes the first word, it extracts useful information from it—such as "pronoun"—by using learned filters, just like CNNs use filters to identify prominent features in images. When the LSTM processes the next word, instead of starting from scratch, it reads the information extracted from the previous word and updates it—possibly adding or removing information. This way, the extraction of information from a sentence is done progressively, word by word. This imitates the way we read sentences from beginning to end and relate the meaning of the words together, even when they are not right next to each other.

These are some examples of deep learning approaches. But there isn't *one* deep learning approach that can be applied to every task. Instead, we need to design a suitable approach for each problem. Sometimes, an approach designed for one task can be recycled and used for other tasks; other times, we need to come up with a novel approach for using machine learning to extract meaning from the data in new, ingenious ways.

Why deep learning is so successful

Machine learning has been used for a long time to tackle difficult tasks like image categorization. However, before deep learning, the process was quite different, and the results were worse.

Back in the day, engineers had to write programs that tried to extract meaningful information from the input before using any machine learning. For example, they would write a program to detect object boundaries in an image and calculate the angles they formed. Afterward, the engineers would extract a list of meaningful features to describe the image, such as "20% of edges are at a 45-degree angle." They would then input these features into the machine learning model instead of the raw image. This made it easier to build traditional machine learning models, such as those with rules of the type "If <u>some input</u> < <u>some value.</u>"

The process of converting raw inputs into a more meaningful representation, known as *feature engineering*, was pretty cumbersome; it involved running slow and convoluted programs. It was also really arbitrary—how could we know whether the feature "proportion of edges at a 45-degree angle" was meaningful for the task at hand? Going by the poor results, it appears that the feature engineering step wasn't coming up with the most useful features. Some engineers ended up blindly generating thousands of features and then running complicated processes to weed out uninformative ones.

Deep learning doesn't require a two-step process that starts with feature engineering before being able to do machine learning—or, it has a much lighter feature engineering process than before. So, the model itself learns a useful representation of the input rather than us humans having to decide which features are important. This has resulted in much higher performance results than before. For example, CNNs for image categorization, trained directly on raw images, consistently beat the old two-step process.

Also, in deep learning, we do a lot of the same stuff—such as applying filters—again and again. So, the whole process can be made really fast by optimizing the repeated operations. In fact, many devices are now equipped with hardware that is especially designed to run deep learning models very quickly. This has dramatically reduced the time required for learning and for using the models.

Does deep learning require human knowledge?

In 2015, DeepMind created their famous deep learning software that beat a human player at the game of Go. Two years later, they created an improved version called AlphaZero with a remarkable feature: According to its creators, the machine learned how to play the game "without human data, guidance, or domain knowledge beyond game rules." Their famous article published in *Nature* was entitled "Mastering the game of Go without human knowledge."[23] This milestone was highly publicized and has led some people to believe that now it's possible to simply tell a computer what you want, and it will then go and learn whatever it takes to achieve it. But is that so?

AlphaZero contains a machine learning model especially trained to calculate the value of possible moves in the game—that is, it can identify which moves are good and which are bad. When playing games against humans, AlphaZero selects high-value moves according to that model.

This model was trained by scanning a large dataset of games. AlphaZero's predecessor used a dataset that contained real games played by humans, and the model was first trained to imitate human players. In AlphaZero, the dataset was created automatically by having the computer play thousands of games against itself and recording which of the pretend players had won the game. Because the dataset didn't contain any human games, AlphaZero's creators claimed it learned "without human knowledge."

The researchers who invented AlphaZero had a clever idea: They treated the Go game board as if it were a tiny image, 19 pixels in width by 19 pixels in height (the typical dimensions of the board). They said this explicitly: "We pass in the board position as a 19 × 19 image."[24]

Afterward, they used a CNN on this image, just like the ones used for image categorization—but instead of trying to distinguish "cat" from "not cat," it tried to distinguish good moves from bad moves.

A CNN was deliberately selected because the assumptions behind CNNs for, say, image categorization were also useful for analyzing a Go board. If you remember, CNNs apply a sequence of filters to identify objects. This is similar to how human players mentally sweep a game board to find interesting patterns (you may have heard of a "fork," a "pin," a "skewer," or a "Queen's Gambit" in chess). Also, CNNs apply filters progressively, trying to identify objects by their parts. Similarly, players of Go mentally sweep the board to identify higher-level patterns, such as groups of stones that are "alive," "dead" and "unsettled."

Choosing to apply a CNN because its underlying assumptions were also useful for Go demonstrates domain knowledge about the task on the part of the researchers. Otherwise, how did they come up with the idea of seeing the board as an image and using a CNN? Why didn't they use one of the many other possible templates for machine learning? Why not use the simpler template from the last chapter, with rules of the type "If some input < some number"? And, while CNNs were effective for Go and other similarly structured games, they are not a good choice for many other tasks.

So, saying that AlphaZero was created "without human data, guidance, or domain knowledge beyond game rules" doesn't seem accurate. A more accurate way of describing the achievement would have been "without data of past human games" or "without imitating human players." Just like we said before, in machine learning it is necessary to use human assumptions to design a specialized template for a task, and AlphaZero is no exception.

The publicity around AlphaZero has also led some people to believe that we can now just simulate data, avoiding the painful process of collecting and labeling data. That's possible with games because one can follow a clear-cut rule to identify who won. But outside the realm of game playing, this is rarely the case. For instance, one cannot create a dataset of correct translations through automatic simulation as necessary to train a machine learning model for translation. If we knew how to generate correct translations automatically, then the problem of automated translation would have already been solved.

Are we building artificial brains?

The neocortex of the brain, which processes visual inputs, consists of a series of six processing layers, where each layer processes its input and passes it on to the next. Experiments have shown that the lowest layer detects simple visual patterns, such as oblique lines and contours. This bears an uncanny resemblance to deep learning's methodology for image categorization, as described above. So, it has become customary to compare deep learning with the human brain, giving the impression that it was directly inspired by the brain or that it actually works similarly to the brain.

The groundwork for CNNs was laid by computer scientist Yann LeCun many years before the deep learning boom. In 1989, he wrote a report introducing the principles of CNNs.[25] The report argued that the idea of applying several filters sequentially seemed highly effective to categorize images. The brain was never mentioned in this report.

A year later, LeCun and his colleagues published a famous article showing the effectiveness of CNNs to categorize handwritten digits.[26] Neither did this article claim that CNNs were inspired by the brain. Instead, it claimed that the CNN's success was due to it being "highly constrained and specifically designed for the task." The authors also said that their decisions were "guided by our prior knowledge about shape recognition." Again, no mention of their being inspired by brain function. The article briefly mentioned that CNNs were "reminiscent" of Neocognitron, which was a brain-inspired method developed eight years earlier by another research group. However, the article seems to imply that CNNs are incidentally similar to Neocognitron, not inspired by it, and Neocognitron was not mentioned again.

As years went by, it became more and more fashionable to compare CNNs with brains. In 2015, LeCun and his colleagues wrote that CNNs "are directly inspired by the classic notions of simple cells and complex cells in visual neuroscience, and the overall architecture is reminiscent of the LGN–V1–V2–V4–IT hierarchy in the visual cortex ventral pathway."[27] And they're not the only ones. Biological explanations of deep learning have become all too common, even if the analogies are loose or have little to do with the brain. For example, a group of researchers from the University of Toronto designed a highly popular method called *dropout*, which improves the way CNNs learn.[28] In their scientific article, they included a lengthy section that tries to link dropout with sexual reproduction and genetics.

But can deep learning truly be likened to the workings of the human brain, or is this more of a publicity stunt?

While the neocortex does have six layers, one after the other, many more processes happen beyond the application of these "filters." For example, some of the layers of the visual cortex also send signals to the thalamus—a structure in the center of the brain. The thalamus is the most "wired" area of the brain; it receives signals from many other parts of the brain, as if it were a sort of relay hub. But the thalamus also sends signals back into the neocortex, creating a complex back-and-forth loop between the two. The role of this loop and many other things about the brain are not yet understood.

So, if we want to compare deep learning to brain function, we must ignore a lot of facts to force a fit.

The dangers of deep learning

As deep learning became the dominant choice for difficult tasks, it made its way into all sorts of applications. Some of them are life critical, such as autonomous vehicles. Researchers have built deep learning models that try to take control of the steering wheel by analyzing video from onboard cameras.[29]

But can we make sure it's safe?

One of the problems of deep learning is its lack of *explainability*. Deep learning models are big and configured automatically, making it hard to know how they come up with their outputs. A CNN, for instance, typically contains hundreds of filters organized in dozens of layers, all of them selected automatically through the learning process. We may be able to understand what the first layer does—say, detect lines or boundaries—but as we move along the subsequent layers of filtering, we can't clearly identify the logic of how things are calculated.

So, using deep learning requires a leap of faith. We trust that it works without knowing exactly how. And we can't guarantee that silly mistakes won't be made at some point—but, as we'll see later on, they do happen. All we can do is test a model repeatedly until we're highly confident—but not sure—that it won't make a silly mistake. And when errors do happen, it's hard to understand why. That's not how we usually do things in life-critical systems; we can usually investigate the causes of an accident (say, from a plane's black boxes) and learn from them, but we can't usually look into the depths of a deep learning program and understand the logic of what we find.

But perhaps one of the most worrying aspects of deep learning is that it can be easily fooled. For example, it is possible to make minor changes to an image, which are imperceptible to the human eye, to fool the model into giving a completely different output.

In 2013, a group of researchers subtly modified images of a school bus, a building and a soap dispenser, and a CNN categorized all three as "ostrich."[30] In 2018, another group of researchers invented a method to alter 3-D models of objects to fool CNNs. They used their method to modify a 3-D model of a turtle in a way that was imperceptible to the human eye. They built the modified turtle with a 3-D printer and took pictures of it from varying viewpoints. The CNN consistently categorized the images as "rifle," even though it correctly categorized pictures of the unmodified object as "turtle."[31]

In a blow to the self-driving car industry, another group of researchers invented a method to make CNNs wrongly categorize street signs.[32] In one instance, they created a poster of a STOP sign especially altered to be wrongly categorized as a Speed Limit 45 sign. They then pasted it over a real street sign, took many pictures of it from various angles and distances, and used a CNN to categorize it. The attack was successful 100% of the time. They also devised a methodology for fooling CNNs that involved pasting small stickers on road signs, which looks like commonplace vandalism. They evaluated this trick using video captured from a moving vehicle, and the CNNs were fooled most of the time.

So, while deep learning has made important strides, it would be naïve to think it's infallible. And, while one may argue that humans are not infallible either, we don't often mistake a turtle for a rifle or a soap dispenser for an ostrich. Being able to trick deep learning so easily has been a bad and unexpected surprise for many. We may even wonder, is current AI truly smart or just a good pretender?

Chapter 3

HOW SMART IS AI?

A few years back, Google Photos released a feature to automatically tag images. A user tried it out with a picture of two black people, and the tag that came out was "gorillas." It went viral. Google "fixed" the software by removing "gorilla," "chimp," "chimpanzee" and "monkey" from the pool of possible tags.

This illustrates a common occurrence in AI. We see that advancements are made overall—computers can play games, categorize objects and guess what you'll write next in an email—yet the most advanced software still makes grave mistakes that a human never would.

Consider the phrase "The box is in the pen." In English, the word "pen" has two distinct meanings: a writing device (✏) and an enclosure where farm animals are kept. When hearing the phrase above, most people imagine a box sitting inside a fenced enclosure on a farm—maybe a crate of eggs or a container of feed. They do not imagine that a box is tightly fit inside a writing "pen" (⬚ → ✏), which indeed sounds a bit ridiculous. However, as of today, if you type "The box is in the pen" into Google Translate to convert the phrase into French, the system picks the French word for a writing pen (*"stylo"*); it doesn't seem to "get" which kind of pen the phrase refers to.

Now, if you type "The chicken is in the pen," Google gets it right, correctly picking the French word for farm enclosure (*"enclos"*). This is because Google uses the context ("chicken") to disambiguate the word "pen" (whereas "box" didn't hint at the farm context). But not so fast! How close to one another do the words "chicken" and "pen" have to be for Google to disambiguate the term correctly? Bad news: As of today, if you type "Where is the chicken? Is it in the pen?" Google mistranslates the second phrase, implying that one is asking whether there is a chicken inside a writing pen (🐔 → ✏?). Try it!

How can AI seem to be getting smarter by the day yet still make such silly mistakes?

In this chapter, we'll discuss why AI is sometimes great and sometimes not. And we'll examine the question of whether current AI could soon become as good as humans at every possible task. We will finish by discussing a recurring dream of the AI community—building fully autonomous, self-driving cars.

What does the model model?

According to neuroscientist Stanislas Dehaene, "To learn is to form an internal model of the external world."[33] Our mental model of the world is remarkably comprehensive; it catalogs thousands of objects, including their appearance, texture, solidity and shape. It also includes descriptions of intangible properties of objects, such as what they're typically used for or where they're found. The model is so precise and comprehensive that we can imagine entire situations that aren't real or even dream about a situation that has never happened in lifelike detail.

The reason we understand the phrase "the box is in the pen" is that we have mental models of boxes and pens, which include information about their shapes and sizes. We also have a mental model of the concept denoted by "in," which describes that for something to be "in" something else, it needs to *fit* inside. That's how we realize that, since a box doesn't fit inside a writing pen, the sort of pen we're referring to must be the other, larger kind.

In machine learning, the current best AI technology, we also build models. But what do these models model? Are they anything like our internal model of the world?

In automated translation, models are built by scanning thousands of parallel text documents written in multiple languages (for instance, Canadian documents written both in French and English). The computer automatically searches these documents for ways in which words are most often translated, usually taking a handful of nearby words for context. For instance, the computer learns that when the word "pen" appears in English with the word "chicken" nearby, the corresponding French text very often uses the word "enclos" (farm enclosure). So, if this happens often enough, a rule is added to the model to output "enclos" for "pen," provided that "chicken" appears nearby.

This model is a representation of how text is most often translated by people—it is built by finding common patterns in previous translations done by people. But knowing how something is often translated is different from knowing how to translate text properly. So, there is a problematic dissonance: The model is built for one thing, to represent how words are often translated, but expected to do something else, to produce good translations.

This happens all the time with machine learning. As of today, machines learn to translate text from previous translations done by humans, they learn to categorize objects in images from objects in images previously categorized by humans, they learn to recognize speech from speech previously transcribed by humans, and so on.

Machines learn statistical regularities in how people have done the job before, but this doesn't give them the broad knowledge of the world required to truly excel at the tasks. So, machines may dupe us for a while because they're good pretenders, but at some point, they end up making silly mistakes a human would never make. At that point, it becomes clear that they are functioning without a model of the world as we know it.

Certain tasks don't require one to know much about the world, so machine learning works just fine. Consider the case of automatically reading license plates in CCTV footage. This task is harder than it seems because of flickering, shadows, occlusions, and so on. However, current AI excels at this task because it doesn't require a sophisticated model of the world. Machine learning successfully identifies statistically recurring patterns in the data, such as "an 8 contains two loops," and that's pretty much all that is required to excel at the task of reading license plates.

Now, consider the task of detecting whether a situation is dangerous from the point of view of a car's driver. This one is much more abstract! A situation's level of danger is not something we learn just from being shown samples of situations and told which ones are dangerous and which ones aren't. Suppose you're driving down the road and you suddenly encounter a flying umbrella in your path—a situation no one told you about in driving school. You'll react according to your knowledge about umbrellas—they're soft so it might be better to hit the object right on rather than swerve. If the object in your way was a horse, on the other hand, you'd probably react differently based on what your model of the world tells you about horses—they are heavy and solid (which isn't something you learned in driving school either), so you may decide to dodge it.

A few years ago, I was driving on a motorway during a massive traffic jam, close to the exit that led to the airport. At one point, an impatient passenger got out of a car in line ahead of me, opened the trunk, took out a suitcase and started walking between other cars toward the exit. It was obvious to me that this person was about to miss a flight and had decided to walk toward the terminal to make it on time.

This is a really strange situation that I'd never encountered before and I had certainly not learned about it in driving school. Yet I could connect the dots based on my knowledge about the world that goes beyond driving. I knew what an airport was, and I knew what missing a flight meant (you can't just board another one five minutes later). I also knew that one brings a suitcase to the airport, and so on.

Tasks like that one—or automated translation—are very difficult for computers because they require a broad understanding of the world, not just samples of how the task has been performed before.

Cows on the beach

A group of researchers from Caltech found out that pictures of animals are very often miscategorized by AI if they are not in their most common environment.[34] For example, they used a popular AI model to categorize a picture of a cow walking on a beach, and the system came up with the following top-5 categories: "not a person," "water," "beach," "outdoors" and "seashore." The cow is nowhere to be found in the output categories, even though it was the most prominent part of the picture, taking up most of the frame. When they repeated the experiment with an image of a cow on grass, "cow" was the number-1 category.

Machine learning operates on a "quantity of evidence" basis. It tries to find statistically recurring patterns in data, and the more evidence of it, the higher the chances of incorporating a relevant rule in the model. In most images of cows, they are standing or lying on the grass. So, machine learning models have learned to associate a cow on the grass with the category "cow," instead of just associating a cow with the category "cow." This is actually a very sensible thing to do, as it is an extremely effective way of correctly categorizing cow images; it is backed by the evidence. But the strategy fails in other, less common situations. As the researchers who brought up the cow issue said, "Current systems are, in essence, glorified pattern-matching machines, rather than intelligent visual learners."

Current AI is akin to memorizing clever gimmicks to pass an exam by analyzing patterns in the wording of questions from previous exams, such as observing that the correct answer to any question about cows tends to be answer choice C, or that "all of the above" tends to be the right answer when it's one of the available choices. This may work sometimes, but it would fail if the teacher asked questions that were very different from the ones on previous exams. If you will, current AI is a sophisticated way of cheating.

Problems like the cows on the beach are unlikely to be reported because researchers tend to use *typical* inputs to analyze their models. So, in the data used to assess the system's performance, there will probably be very few, if any, cows pictured not on grass. This way, epic fails like cows on the beach are downplayed.

Also, researchers tend to just *count* the number of errors, reporting figures like "5% error rate," without considering how bad they are. But if we merely count the number of errors, grave mistakes receive the same weight as minor ones, and problems like the cow-on-the-beach situation go unnoticed (not detecting the cow at all bears the same weight as, say, mistaking it for a bull). I saw a LinkedIn survey which went as follows: "What would you trust more, a human surgeon with 80% success rate or an AI surgeon with 90% success rate?" It is true that technology has made us safer in many ways and can help us prevent human error. However, I'd be wary of those figures as they're just counting mistakes instead of qualifying them. What if the AI surgeon is more successful in terms of the overall count but sometimes makes unexpected mistakes a human typically doesn't, like botching an easy surgery? And what if we can't trace and explain mistakes made by AI in the same way we would with humans?

Assessing the power of AI just by counting mistakes in typical situations might be okay for some applications. But, in other cases, it is critical to have good performance in unprecedented or unexpected scenarios. The Caltech researchers gave a few examples of such applications: "Self-driving cars navigating new cities, rovers exploring new planets, security cameras installed in new buildings, and assistive technologies installed in new homes."

Human learning vs. machine learning

A non-techie friend of mind was quite surprised when he found out that thousands of images of cats were required to have a computer effectively identify cats; he thought that, with all the publicity around AI, current technology was much "smarter" than that.

Machine learning, as it stands now, needs to analyze many samples to learn effectively. Neuroscientist Stanislas Dehaene wrote, "The state of the art in machine learning involves running millions, even billions, of training attempts on computers. [...] In this contest, the infant brain wins hands down: babies do not need more than one or two repetitions to learn a new word."[35]

That's one of the most striking differences between human learning and current machine learning—humans can accomplish more learning from limited data. When a parent points out a butterfly to a toddler and says, "That's a butterfly," the toddler may learn the word right away.

It appears that the reason why babies learn from little data is that they utilize a wide array of learning shortcuts. One of them, for example, is the process of elimination, which babies start using as early as 16 months of age.[36] For instance, suppose a parent points at a table full of objects from a distance and says, "Bring me the book." If the toddler doesn't know the word "book" yet but knows the names of all the other objects, they will be able to figure out which object is the book and also learn the new word. There's even a famous case of a dog, Rico, who learned the name of 200 objects and, when asked to fetch an unknown object from a room, he correctly identified the item by process of elimination.[37]

Babies also use shortcuts to focus their attention on the most important object in the scene, making it easier to learn from a single example. For instance, when a parent says, "That's a butterfly," there are probably many other objects around that the word could refer to, such as trees, clouds and the blue sky in the background. In current machine learning, the computer would typically have to browse many different butterfly images until realizing that the common object in all the images is a colorful bug and thus learn the word (and this can still lead to a cow-on-grass situation). Instead, the baby follows the parent's gaze or pointer finger to focus its attention just on the butterfly.[38]

If we wanted AI to match human skills, it would have to use data more efficiently for learning. However, most machine learning still delivers an underwhelming performance in that regard. Some researchers have tried to improve it, for example, by including an attention component that makes the computer focus more on some parts of the input than others. This may have improved performance in some cases, but there is still a long way to go. Equipping machine learning with the wide array of learning shortcuts used by humans—or finding equally effective alternatives—is still an open problem.

It's never-ending

What happens if we take action to fix AI's epic fails? What if we went through and corrected for the poor translations, people identified as gorillas and gigantic cows totally ignored?

It seems to me that every time an epic fail is fixed, another one pops up. Imagine someone fixed the problem with translating "the box is in the pen." It won't take long until you can fool the system again; just find another word with multiple meanings. If you can't fool the system right away, split the phrase in two and add a bit of ambiguity with a pronoun.

For instance, if I type "The dog's bark was pleasant," Google translates it correctly into French. But if I type "The dog was cute. I even thought its bark was pleasant," it gets it wrong, translating "bark" as if I was speaking about the coating of a tree. If the creators of this system somehow fixed the problem with the word "bark," it wouldn't take too long for you to find another word that breaks it. As journalist Tom Siegfried put it, "Some artificial intelligence is smart until it's dumb."[39]

Even the most advanced machine learning models can

be broken. Consider the case of GPT-3, a highly popular model trained to predict the next words in text. This model, built by the research lab OpenAI, can be used to generate entire documents and even answer questions. It was trained by scanning billions of sentences gathered from the internet. So, as usual, it learned how to do the job by imitating how humans have done it before. The model produces text that is grammatically correct and is remarkably sound at first sight. However, we can find epic fails if we poke it a bit harder. It may take a little bit longer to find them, as the software becomes better, but you can still trick it nevertheless.

One way to fool GPT-3 is to ask it trick questions that include wrong assumptions. These falsehoods should be easy for us humans to spot thanks to our extensive mental models, but AI is not that knowledgeable. These are some examples:

Q: Who was the president of the UK last year?
A: The president of the UK was not elected last year.

Q: Why isn't Donald Trump scheduled to meet the Italian king?
A: Donald Trump is not scheduled to meet the Italian king because he is not the president of the United States.

Q: Why can't I run a 2-mile marathon?
A: Because it's too long.

Another way to trick GPT-3 is to ask useless questions that require world knowledge to answer but are too weird to be commonly asked. Since GPT-3 has learned from data collected from the Internet, it won't easily find answers to those questions. These are some examples:

Q: Can you see the Northern Lights in Ecuador?
A: Yes, you can see the Northern Lights in Ecuador in the northernmost part of the country, near the border with Colombia.

Q: Does an anaconda fit inside a shopping mall?
A: No, an anaconda is too large to fit inside a shopping mall. An anaconda can grow up to 25 feet long, which is much too large to fit in a shopping mall.

Q: How old is my watch?
A: Your watch is as old as the time it displays.

Q: How hot should the water be in Celsius to melt my phone?
A: The water should be at 0 degrees Celsius to melt your phone.

Q: Why doesn't a peeled hard-boiled egg leak?
A: Because the eggshell is no longer there to protect it.

Mathematical and logic puzzles also lead GPT-3 astray, especially if we formulate them in a way that requires world knowledge to understand:

Q: If I climb three flights of stairs and then I stand on my feet for three seconds, how far am I from my starting point?
A: Six feet.

Q: I jump three steps to the right. Then, as I'm just about to jump two steps to the left, I decide to stand still instead. How far am I from my starting point?
A: You are one step to the right of your starting point.

Finally, AI may struggle with long-winded phrases that require memory of something said long ago to answer or that contain ambiguous pronouns.[40] Here's one example:

Q: Mrs. March gave the mother tea and gruel, while she dressed the little baby as tenderly as if it had been her own. Who's the baby's mother?
A: Mrs. March.

In November 2022, OpenAI released a highly publicized chatbot called ChatGPT, which is based on an improved version of GPT-3. Among other things, ChatGPT was especially designed to challenge incorrect premises. Sometimes, its answers to the above questions are more satisfactory:

Q: How old is my watch?

A: I'm sorry, but I am not able to answer that question as I am a large language model trained by OpenAI and do not have access to information about your watch. I do not have the ability to see or interact with physical objects, and I am only able to provide information based on my pre-existing knowledge. To determine the age of your watch, you would need to consult the manufacturer or a professional watchmaker.

However, its weaknesses are still observed in many other cases, such as the following:

Q: Why isn't Donald Trump scheduled to meet the Italian king?

A: I'm sorry, but I cannot answer that question as my training only goes up until 2021, and I am not able to browse the internet for current information. I am only able to provide information based on my pre-existing knowledge.

Q: Why wasn't Donald Trump scheduled to meet the Italian king in 2020?

A: I'm sorry, but I am not able to browse the internet and therefore do not have information on Donald Trump's schedule. As a large language model trained by OpenAI, my knowledge is based solely on the text that I have been trained on, and I do not have access to real-time information or current events. My knowledge is limited to general facts and information that were widely known up until 2021.

Q: Why can't I run a 2-mile marathon?

A: There could be many reasons why you may not be able to run a 2-mile marathon. Some possible reasons could include a lack of physical fitness or training, medical conditions that affect your ability to run, or simply not having enough time to prepare for the race.

Q: Does an anaconda fit inside a shopping mall?

A: It is not possible for an anaconda to fit inside a shopping mall, as anacondas are typically much larger than the size of a shopping mall. Anacondas are some of the largest snakes in the world, and can grow to be over 20 feet long and weigh over 100 pounds. A shopping mall, on the other hand, is a large indoor commercial building that typically has multiple floors and is designed for retail shopping and other activities. An anaconda would not be able to fit inside a shopping mall, even if it was empty.

Q: Why doesn't a peeled hard-boiled egg leak?

A: A peeled hard-boiled egg does not leak because the membrane that surrounds the egg white has been removed along with the shell. The membrane helps to hold the egg together and prevents the egg white from leaking out.

When the shell and the membrane are removed, the egg white is no longer contained and can leak out if not handled carefully.

I'm sure some of these answers will improve in the future. But I'm also confident we'll keep finding other ways to fool the machine. Note that no piece of AI has ever passed a Turing test, meaning that it was indistinguishable from a human in conversation.

As AI keeps improving, the number of problematic cases keeps shrinking and thus it becomes more usable. However, the problematic cases never seem to disappear. It's as if you took a step that brings you 80% of the way toward a destination, and then another step covering 80% of the remaining distance, and then another step to get 80% closer, and so on; you'd keep getting closer to your destination but never reach it.

It also seems that each step is much harder than the previous ones; each epic fail we find seems to require an increasingly complicated solution to fix.

If you speak with AI fanatics, you'll see that some refuse to acknowledge that the problem at the root of epic fails is that AI isn't all that smart. Instead, they blame it on something else. The most popular scapegoat is data—they say that data wasn't abundant enough or adequate for the task.

In the case of the cow on the beach, AI fanatics would argue that the dataset didn't contain enough pictures of cows in varied contexts. They'd say that, if the system had had a chance to see pictures of cows that are not on grass, it would have picked up what a cow really is. That might well solve the cow issue. But what about the next problem AI runs into?

The pathway to artificial general intelligence

Will computers in the future be able to perform any intellectual task as well as a human can? If that happens, we would have attained *artificial general intelligence*—or AGI.

It is worth noting that reaching AGI doesn't require building humanoid robots that look like us. What AGI requires is a known methodology to reach human-level performance in every task, even though we may not implement all of it in a single place or in a robot with human-like appearance.

The term AGI has become quite popular over the past few years and there's been a lot of speculation around it. Futurist Ray Kurzweil, for instance, predicted that AGI will be attained in 2029,[41] and Elon Musk said on Twitter that he'd be surprised if we don't have AGI by then.[42]

To reach AGI, computers would have to match human performance in the most challenging tasks, including language comprehension. As we've seen throughout this chapter, machine learning, which is currently the highest-performing type of AI, does not accomplish that. So, the missing piece to reach AGI is not just some practical limitation, say, that computers aren't fast enough or that we don't have enough data. Faster computers or more data might be necessary, but they wouldn't be enough. In order to reach AGI, someone would need to discover a new, unprecedented methodology, since machine learning as it is today falls short. So, what AGI requires is innovation.

But how can we know if or when the necessary innovation will take place?

A common response to that question, and a reason to support the view that AGI is imminent, is the *law of accelerating returns*. This law, popularized by Ray Kurzweil, describes how technology evolves. It states that the rate of technological change accelerates as time passes. This leads to an exponential growth in technology's capabilities, similar to the effect of compound interests in savings or the initial expansion of an epidemic. The law acknowledges that technological growth does sometimes reach a plateau. However, it states that each time a plateau is reached, there is a "paradigm shift" or a "key event" that propels technological growth upward once again and at an even faster rate.

But the law of accelerating returns, however fascinating, should be taken with a grain of salt; it is more alchemy than science. The law is based on observations about past events, but the evidence to support it seems anecdotal. For example, Kurzweil collected a list of events that some anthropologists, astronomers, and Encyclopedia Brittanica considered "important" throughout history and used this list to show that important events have occurred at an accelerating pace. But how can we be sure that this selection of events accurately reflects the evolution of technology? Kurzweil also illustrated exponential growth by charting on a graph key events like "homo sapiens," "wheel," and "personal computer," which he selected himself based on his own "views of key developments in biological and technological history."[43] It is even hard to find a precise definition of the law; its proponents tend to speak of technological "growth" or "evolution" without stating what it describes exactly. Kurzweil even tells us that we are "beginning to reach the knee of the curve" [44] without specifying what the curve is or how exactly we can identify the "knee" in it.

The law is often used to make predictions about the future of technology, including the famous *singularity*—a hypothetical breakthrough moment in the future when we'll witness remarkably fast technological growth. If we apply the law to AGI, then the missing piece of the puzzle will necessarily be discovered soon, since we've recently reached many AI milestones and we can only expect the pace of advances to accelerate. In a conversation I had with a person who works at Google DeepMind, he insisted he "strongly believed" AGI was imminent due to how fast progress has been made by his company in the last few years.

We must note, however, that these predictions assume that innovation will continue at an ever-increasing rate. That is, we must believe that the law of accelerating returns will continue to be valid in the future. This seems hard to justify.

How can we be sure that exponential growth will be sustained? How can we be sure, for instance, that there won't be a prolonged period of stagnation? Or how can we be sure that limiting factors, such as energy or money, won't slow things down? Innovation is, by definition, something that cannot be predicted. If you told me that you're 100% sure that AGI will be reached in one year, I'd ask you which new methodology has been discovered to achieve that. And if you told me that it hasn't been discovered yet, but that you're 100% sure that it will be, I'd ask you how you can know that or what you're basing your prediction on. There is no way to know when something new will be discovered. We can predict how long it will take to build a bridge because we know how to build bridges, but we cannot predict when an unprecedented discovery will be made. The proof of this is in the pudding—Nick Bostrom writes in his book *Superintelligence*, "Historically, AI researchers have not had a strong record of being able to predict the rate of advances in their own field or the shape that such advances would take."[45]

There is no clear pathway yet toward artificial general intelligence. We might be positively surprised in the near future, but it is conceivable that, even if possible in principle, it will not happen anytime soon. This is reminiscent of nuclear fusion, which seems like a promising way of producing electricity, but no one has found a method to do it efficiently, and no one knows when, if ever, that will happen.

Case study: Self-driving cars

A self-driving car would be *fully autonomous* if it could drive itself on any road and in the presence of pedestrians, animals, and other vehicles (autonomous or not). One of the most prominent promises made by AI proponents since the 2010s is the fulfillment of this dream. Elon Musk said it in 2015: "My guess for when we will have full autonomy is approximately three years."[46]

A lot of the enthusiasm about self-driving cars comes from the observation that human error is the cause of most traffic accidents. This makes it seem like the bar that AI has to clear isn't all that high—self-driving cars just need to be less bad drivers than humans. In 2017, an article on *Wired* said, "Put them on the roads when they cause fewer deaths overall than human drivers. If humans cause 37,462 car deaths a year, and driverless cars cause 37,461, let 'em roll."[47] A few months later, another article predicted that more than 300,000 deaths could be prevented in the U.S. in ten years "through fully autonomous cars by eliminating driver error."[48] Indeed, improving road safety would be a remarkable achievement, and it's been one of the main motives behind the development of self-driving cars.[49] Also, novel technology has a good track record of making us safer, from seat belts to airbags. But is it possible to build safe, fully autonomous cars with our current AI knowledge?

From our discussion in this chapter, you can guess that my answer to that question is no. Driving is a difficult task that requires a comprehensive mental model of the world and the ability to interpret unprecedented situations. Current AI isn't very good at either. The excessive focus on *counting* errors, like the number of deaths per year in the above quotes, may have made the task seem easily attainable. But merely counting errors conceals some of the greatest challenges of current AI, like the fact that it sometimes makes unexpected goofs that humans don't usually make or that it sometimes gets completely confused by uncommon yet simple "cow-on-the-beach" situations.

As companies kept trying to build self-driving cars through the 2010s and into the 2020s, the shortcomings of AI started to become evident. Waymo, one of the foremost companies in the industry, soon realized that current AI cannot cope well with out-of-the-ordinary situations. So, they started training their AI models with examples of atypical actors in the road environment, including "a construction worker waist deep in a manhole, someone in a horse costume, [and] a man standing on the corner spinning an arrow-shaped sign."[50]

One may wonder what would occur when *other* strange things happen that haven't been explicitly shown to the AI model. We may already know the answer; in 2021, a Waymo car got confused by a row of traffic cones in a construction zone and came to a complete stop. The car blocked traffic in Chandler, Arizona, for a long period of time and technicians had to rush to its rescue.[51]

Enthusiasm about fully autonomous cars may have started to wane. In 2021, two journalists from Bloomberg wrote, "Waymo Is 99% of the Way to Self-Driving Cars. The Last 1% Is the Hardest."[52] That last one percent is precisely the never-ending remainder of challenging cases that we discussed above.

Elon Musk also seems equally disappointed of late. After moving the goalpost several times, he finally acknowledged, in 2021, "Generalized self-driving is a hard problem, as it requires solving a large part of real-world AI. I didn't expect it to be so hard, but the difficulty is obvious in retrospect."[53]

Autonomous vehicles in highly controlled and predictable environments have existed for a long time, including autopilots in aircraft and autonomous trains in urban transit systems. You've likely experienced one or both of those before in your own travels. Because planes and trains exist in controlled environments (a sky with clearly delimited airspaces and routes, under the direction of air traffic control, and along a set of railroad tracks), they don't require "a model of the world" to operate. But no fully autonomous vehicles have yet been built outside of controlled environments.

So, whenever you see an announcement of a fully autonomous car, I suggest you read the fine print. Consider this headline from 2021: "France approves fully autonomous bus for driving on public roads in a European first."[54] It turns out that this vehicle is a shuttle bus that runs inside a quiet campus driving back and forth on a fixed route. The route is

600 meters (0.4 miles) in length. The vehicle uses a GPS to drive along the fixed path at a rather slow speed, and it stops whenever its sensors detect an object nearby.

Unless something radically new is discovered, you'll likely observe a similar pattern when autonomous vehicles are announced around the world: they will either require constant human supervision or operate in a restricted and controlled environment.

Chapter 4

BUSINESS

In this chapter, I'll tell you the untold story of AI in business. I'm sure you've heard the nice version of the story, about how AI adds value and that more and more businesses are adopting it. You've probably also heard that many companies have become "AI powered," "AI enabled" or "AI driven." And that is certainly true in many cases.

But behind every successful AI project, there are many stories of disappointment, unfulfilled expectations and, sometimes, lies. You won't often hear those sorts of stories, but I think it's important to know both sides, lest we end up with an overly optimistic view of the AI world.

The story told in this chapter is based on my personal experience working in data science—a field that tries to build AI products to make a positive impact on businesses. I'll tell you about how companies get swept up in the frenzy and pour millions into AI projects then play it fast and loose with the truth when things don't go their way. I have changed some details in the stories to preserve my former employers' and clients' anonymity, but the essence of the stories remains unchanged.

After seeing many AI projects at many companies not go as expected, I've noticed that the process is quite predictable. In fact, I've identified five clear stages that lead to a project's failure. Let's walk through these five stages. It isn't pretty, so brace yourself!

Stage 1: Putting the cart before the horse

A few years ago, an entrepreneur contacted me for some advice on an AI project. When we met, he told me he was a big fan of cars and had a lot of connections in that industry, so he wanted to build a company to "do something with AI and cars." He asked me if I could help him find a problem he could solve with AI within the automotive sector.

That's entrepreneurship (and engineering) upside down! In an ideal world, one has a problem *first* and finds the best solution for it *afterward*. However, in the world of AI, very often people first bring the solution to the table—AI—without even knowing what they'll do with it.

You may have heard the tale about a FedEx processing facility that one day had a complete shutdown due to some unknown error. They brought in the best expert they could find to fix the issue. When the guy arrived, it took him two minutes to fix the problem—all he had to do was tighten a loose screw. He charged $10,000 for the job—$1 for turning the screw and $9,999 for knowing which screw to turn. While this story is likely untrue, it illustrates what an engineer is supposed to do: Find the best way to solve an existing problem.

Well, in the world of AI, things don't always work like that. You'll see more than a few companies that just *want* to use AI. It's as if the engineer at the FedEx facility had a favorite screw to turn that he would fiddle with at any job instead of searching for the one that needed turning. When companies do things this way, they are putting the solution before the problem, or the cart before the horse.

One of the craziest experiences I've had in the corporate world was when I was asked to be a sort of "spy." This company had created a team whose goal was to "promote the use of AI in the business," which is an exquisite example of putting the cart before the horse. This team would interview employees across the organization and show them how AI could benefit them. They would then build a prototype of an AI product to prove its benefits and then promote it within the organization.

The business was not happy with the team though; they sensed they were doing poor-quality work and had questionable work ethics. But, for political reasons, there wasn't much they could do to make changes to the team.

So, they gave me the assignment of joining that team to give a helping hand with the AI workload. However, I had a secret mission: to try to influence the team to change the way they worked and have them implement better AI practices. The leader of that team didn't know about this secret assignment of mine.

I probably only accepted the assignment because it caught me off guard. I did it for a very short time, but it was enough for me to see what the real problem was. Since the team's goal was to "promote AI," they *had* to find problems to solve with AI or else the team wouldn't be able to justify its own existence. So, they kept trying to push AI at all costs. For that, they built poor-quality prototypes to "prove" that AI worked, without doing basic due diligence. They also kept purchasing expensive subscriptions to external AI software that locked them into long-term contracts. The real problem was that this company had created an official cart-before-horse team.

I witnessed another remarkable example of the same backwards phenomenon at a boutique consulting company that specialized in one particular AI method, reinforcement learning. Since that was their area of expertise, they wanted to push it everywhere. In particular, they had recently signed a contract with one of Europe's largest airlines to optimize their online advertising by using reinforcement learning.

They invited me to work for them to build a prototype of

their proposed advertising software. They didn't disclose too many details about the intended solution ahead of my start, and I didn't ask too many questions because, quite naively, I assumed that a team of AI experts would have thought it through (I'm not sure they would have answered my questions anyway, as companies tend to be quite protective of their methods).

It was my first day working with this company. I got to work, and I was shocked to find out that they hadn't even thought about what to do next. The proposal was just "reinforcement learning to improve advertising." No further detail or even a concrete use case. They didn't even know which kind of advertising channel they would be working on. They had managed to sell the methodology to the airline without specifying what they would do with it, and the airline was willing to pay them the big bucks. How crazy is that?

After some deliberation, the managers picked a use case: They decided to use reinforcement learning to automatically allocate money to different Facebook ads based on their past performance. But that's what Facebook already does! Facebook uses a flavor of reinforcement learning to allocate more budget to winning ads. Why would we reinvent the wheel? And how would we be able to beat Facebook at what they'd been doing for a long time, especially considering they had access to a lot of data that we didn't? It was probably lucky that the project got canceled due to COVID-19 because it wasn't going to end well.

There must be an explanation for this frenzy, a reason why everyone tries to push AI everywhere. I think one of the main reasons is that saying you're working on AI is a great way of raising funding from private investors and the government with a low level of accountability.

Have a look at this communication from the European Commission in 2018:

> It is key for Europe to identify and invest in the next generation of AI and to roll it out widely. One important element is making available sufficient investment for start-ups in their early stage as well as for companies in their scale-up phase. To this end, the Commission aims at making available resources for start-ups and innovators in AI and block-chain [...]

Who wouldn't want to jump on that gravy train? Also, the European Union and other institutions are not just handing out loans, they're handing out grants that companies don't have to pay back—they're giving them free money. Also, many countries offer tax credits for innovative technological projects, and working on AI is a sure way to obtain them. My first employer, for instance, only spent an effective 10% of my yearly salary to employ me because they gained tax credits for my work. They didn't have strong AI use cases and their priorities were mostly elsewhere, but at that price why not give it a try? That's cart-before-horse in all its glory.

My experience has shown me that these sources of funding require little accountability. Very often, all a company needs to do is file a report many years later to say how it went. I have personally seen companies use the money for something else entirely, waving it off with the suggestion that they'd "think of something" when the time came to file a report.

AI is also a good bait to bring talent to a company. Because everyone is speaking about AI, employees want to tick that box in their résumés. So, a great way to lure applicants to a job is to say it involves AI (even if it doesn't—you'll figure something out later on!). For example, once a company interviewed me on the phone for an AI position. Only when they flew me in for an on-site interview did they confess that the job involved no AI at all. They argued they would like to "explore the potential" of AI down the line and claimed that I'd be the right person for it when the time came. This role was based in a remote Nordic town where the sun barely rises in winter, and my impression was that they were finding it difficult to get anyone interested in moving there, so they spruced up the description a little.

But putting the cart before the horse is not always a cynical attempt to get money or talent. Very often, businesspeople genuinely believe—or are led to believe—that AI is a silver bullet that can solve any problem. In the most extreme case, they may even think AI can do the impossible.

For example, I once worked for a company that was suffering from a troublesome problem: Clients would book a visit from a cable installer to their homes, but sometimes the installer would knock on the door and no one would answer (perhaps because the client forgot about the appointment). A team of analysts was trying to improve this process. After analyzing the data over and over, they came to the conclusion that those unfortunate events were unpredictable—there were no common characteristics among the clients that didn't open the door. "So, we must use AI!" some manager in the company suggested, as if it were some sort of crystal ball that would magically see what the analysis didn't. Sometimes AI does identify patterns that others overlook, but here that seemed a very long shot. You'll hear how this project went in a bit.

Finally, let's not forget the most stellar example of putting the cart before the horse: the entire industry of self-driving cars. Since AI seemed to be getting better and better, some people thought it would soon be able to excel at *any* difficult human task. So, they decided that they should use it to tackle one of the most difficult tasks—driving. They thought AI would necessarily solve this problem, and all that was required to get it done was to put a handful of expensive engineers in a room for long enough. With milestones being pushed further out every year, the results speak for themselves.

Stage 2: Errors go unnoticed

After deciding to use AI, the next thing these companies will do is build an initial version or prototype of the promising AI product. Unfortunately, it often happens that the product is broken, and nobody knows it. But how can someone build something broken and not realize it? That happens a lot in AI, possibly more so than in any other field, and there is a clear reason for it.

In traditional software development, a tiny error—or *bug*—tends to get magnified. For example, a silly coding mistake results in a horrific blue screen, in a webpage that doesn't load or in an incomprehensible error message (I'm sure you've run into one before). Bugs can be sneaky sometimes, but in general people realize sooner rather than later that something is wrong because minor errors tend to get overblown.

In AI, it's the exact opposite: A tiny methodological error tends to make it seem like everything works better than it does. To understand why this happens, keep in mind that AI nowadays involves machine learning—so the computer is actively trying to find meaningful things in data. If we're not careful enough, the machine will end up finding illusory patterns that don't exist or cheat to attain its goal (like in the cow-on-grass situation from the last chapter).

Let's revisit our friends the cable installers for a concrete example of this. This was the company that wanted to use AI to predict whether a client would forget their appointment with the cable installer and not be there to open the door. They decided to use machine learning to crack this puzzle. So, they took a database containing a long history of real past appointments and whether the client was there to open the door or not. Each appointment contained information such as the date, time and the client type—whether it was a business or a residence.

Machine learning was used to automatically scan that data and find rules to predict the outcome of the cable installation visit. The hope was that the system would discover, for instance, that clients of a certain type or at a certain location were more likely not to answer the door. These associations would then be used to preemptively call clients deemed unreliable to reconfirm appointments.

The company assessed the system against the record of past appointments, and it seemed that it was able to successfully determine which clients were unreliable.

At this point, I was hired to take up that prototype, make it better and promote it to the people who'd ultimately use it. I soon found out the system was cheating to assess clients. I discovered that the most important association rule learned by the machine was the following: "If the client type equals 'NULL' then the client will not open the door; otherwise, they will open the door." But "NULL" meant that there was no data about the client type (which in normal circumstances should have been "house" or "business"). How could the absence of data be so useful to make predictions about people's flakiness? Something smelled fishy.

It turns out that the historical data regarding successful appointments was prepared by one person, and the data for unsuccessful appointments was prepared by another person. The person in charge of unsuccessful appointments was using outdated client information and, as a result, it often contained "NULL" for the client type. This means that when no one had opened the door, the data contained "NULL" much more often, which was a good way to "predict" that no one had opened the door. These predictions wouldn't work in real life because the "NULL" values were only introduced after knowing whether an appointment had been successful or not. This is called *data leakage*—information about what you want to predict is leaked to the inputs used by the model. The machine identified this shady pattern and used it to cheat instead of learning something useful that would help make real predictions. It's as if students realized that a teacher always puts the correct answer as the first option in a multiple-choice exam, so they can pass the test by always ticking "(a)" all the time instead of learning the material.

Unfortunately, once the "NULL" issue was fixed, the system became useless at assessing clients' reliability. (If you remember from the previous section, even business analysts thought this was impossible to predict.) On the flip side, the problem was detected early on, but this isn't always the case....

Let me tell you a story of a large company that conducted an experiment repeatedly the wrong way *for two years*, falsely proving that AI was adding value to the business.

This company was an online store that used AI to automatically pick which product to show at the top of the search results. Showing relevant recommendations at the top tends to generate extra revenue for a business—after all, when was the last time you scrolled all the way down or visited pages two and three before deciding on your purchase?

After developing their innovative, AI-based technology, this company had to prove it was worth the effort. For that, they used A/B testing, a technique where different users are shown different versions of the webpage at random to measure and compare the effect on users. This is similar to a clinical trial to approve a vaccine, in which some people get the vaccine while others get a placebo. In this case, the recommendations coming from the AI technology were shown to some users, while naïve recommendations—the cheapest products on top—were shown to others.

The thing is, showing different versions of the webpage at random leads to poor user experience; if the same person were to visit the store multiple times, they would see different things recommended on top, which is annoying. So, instead of using randomness on every visit, they mapped users from certain randomly selected cities to the AI version of the software, while users from other cities would land on the "placebo" version. Since users don't change cities very often, they'd usually see the same recommended products at the top of the page on repeated visits to the website.

When they measured the results, it seemed that users that landed on the AI version of the webpage were much more likely to buy than the others in the control group. For about two years, the team in charge kept "proving" this result, which meant that the team's work was bringing a lot of value to the organization.

But, at one point, things took a dark turn.... It was discovered that the way of picking users was quite biased. The AI version was assigned disproportionately more to users in affluent countries (say, Monaco and Switzerland). So, it was now unclear whether AI itself was adding value or it just looked better because it was mostly used by wealthy shoppers.

The experiment was botched. It was like a vaccine trial where the placebo is given to smokers and the true vaccine to non-smokers, thus invalidating any conclusions about the vaccine's effectiveness for improving people's health.

Unfortunately, methodological errors like this are quite common and they tend to lead to overconfidence in AI. The solution is to set up an impeccable validation process so that errors can be caught early on. However, I've seen that sometimes people resist this. It's almost as if they simply want to believe that AI is working.

Stage 3: Explosive growth

After a company builds a first prototype of an AI product and it seems to be successful, they tend to immediately grow their AI function—they hire several new employees at lightning-fast speed and launch entirely new teams devoted to AI. I've seen explosive growth like this many times.

Consider the example I just gave of the company with the botched validation study that "proved" that online shoppers (who happened to be mostly affluent) bought more from AI-based recommendations. The initial prototype was built by two curious employees who were trying out machine learning for the first time within the division. When the first series of (botched) experiment results came out, the management was highly enthusiastic. They thought that if the numbers looked so good with such little effort, it could only get much better if the task was taken seriously. So, they created a dedicated team for that use case and grew it to 12 people in one year.

This is not an uncommon pattern—a team exploding from zero to double digits after management sees a hint that AI may work. Two weeks ago, a company called me because they were looking for a data scientist to join a team of 10 new hires, including data scientists, data engineers, product managers and a corporate communications specialist. I asked them what stage they were at and they said an engineer had to finish up a rough proof of concept of the product idea, but they were highly confident that it would work.

I suspect that one reason why managers go crazy and build big AI teams so fast is confirmation bias. After putting the cart before the horse because everyone said AI would be amazing, the slightest victory (however broken the prototype or botched the experiment) convinces them of AI's potential.

But an entire team built on a minor victory is like a barely balanced house of cards. What if the initial prototype's success was due to a methodological error and not its own merit? What's going to happen when the product doesn't meet expectations and more than 10 people have just been hired to continue developing it? What happens next isn't pretty....

Stage 4: Telling lies

A well-known, multinational company wanted to build an AI-powered system to help their executives make important decisions about the business. The decisions were high-impact stuff, the kind that can make many people lose their jobs in the blink of an eye. This system was supposed to output recommendations to those executives. I joined the project for a few months on a fixed-term contract.

This was a typical cart-before-horse situation because they blindly assumed AI would work, without first considering whether the project was technically feasible. They asked a data scientist who worked in the company to come up with an AI-based solution to the task. He came up with a very complicated and unfeasible idea, which tried to have AI do the impossible with no data. The managers (all business executives without any tech knowledge) didn't understand the technicalities and didn't get a second opinion. They went ahead with the project, hiring several new people to work on building this solution.

The approach was so complicated that it took almost an entire year and seven figures in spending to get the preliminary results. That's about the time I joined the project to help improve the existing product and package it so it could be used by the executives. I soon realized that the recommendations made by the system were nonsensical and it would be very hard to fix, but I was told that we couldn't do anything about it because the executives were already trying out the tool.

Brace yourself for what's coming next because it's pretty crazy.

In our meetings with the executives, they often compared the recommendations made by our system with decisions they'd already made or were about to make. When there was a mismatch between the recommendations and their decisions, they'd let us know. They'd say something like, "Hmmm.... But I already made this business decision and the AI says I shouldn't. Why is this contradicting me?"

The leaders of my team would apologize, suggesting there was probably a mistake or a bug on our end, and they asked us data scientists to "fix" it. For that, they made us add a layer to override the outputs of the AI so that it gave the "correct" recommendation in that instance (what the executive wanted to hear). So, the AI-based recommendations were in fact carefully tailored to support the decisions that the executives made on their own.

In a meeting, I raised my concerns with the product manager, telling her (again) that it would probably never be possible to build the product as intended and make real recommendations. She replied, "Well, we cannot say that we cannot build this. We said a year ago that this was possible, so now we can't say it's not."

I asked, "Why not?"

She kept repeating the mantra, "We can't say it's not possible if we said it was."

So, the fabrication of outputs continued on and on, to the point that the recommendations were so tampered with that the underlying AI was barely used—the software would produce the same outputs if we eliminated the AI altogether (the bit that had cost millions to develop) and just outputted the handmade recommendations we'd added on top, the ones carefully written to please the executives.

The whole thing got so shady that we, the hands-on AI practitioners, were not allowed to speak directly with the executives that used the product. I once replied to an innocuous email that an executive sent directly to me with a question about how to use the product, and I was scolded for doing so. Instead, all communication had to be mediated by the team leaders, who censored and rewrote sentences to make sure we didn't reveal what we were truly doing. (But maybe the executives already knew it. Who knows!) Our duplicity reminds me of the story of Theranos, the company that had allegedly built a revolutionary machine to test blood samples at home but turned out to be a big fraud. The AI team of this company was a small-scale Theranos.

One day, I was asked to give a PowerPoint presentation to introduce our AI tool to some other executives in the company who hadn't used it yet. I had to pretend it was amazing and fill the slides with buzz words while avoiding any unflattering details. My presentation slides were fine-combed by my superiors to make sure I didn't somehow reveal the truth. Apparently, I gave a stellar presentation; one of the attendees sent an email across the organization to express how impressed he was. He said he felt like he was "speaking with rocket scientists." (This was about the time Elon Musk sent his first rocket to space, hence the analogy.) I couldn't help but giggle: Our tool was *completely bogus* yet he compared it to rocket science!

One may think that at this point, when the weaknesses of the product were known, the team leaders would have scaled back. However, they kept hiring more people onto the project team. I have seen this several times—an AI team keeps asking for more budget and more employees, even when things aren't working. They fear that, if they do otherwise, the rest of the organization will realize that things aren't going as well as promised, putting the future of the team in jeopardy.

So, in my experience, the explosive growth of AI teams does not end when people notice the AI isn't as good as expected.

This experience made me quite miserable because I felt like I was participating in a big scam. I felt I was compromising my ethics. I did my best for as long as I could, and I'm happy it's long over now. Phew!

Unfortunately, that's just one of the several times I've seen companies play it fast and loose with the truth when it comes to AI. Remember the online retail company with the botched experiment that "proved" AI's value with affluent clients? One day, one of the new hires in the team started suspecting there was an error in the experimentation process. That's an awkward position to be in—to be questioning the supposedly promising experiment results that had led to the expansion of the team, landing her and another 10 people their jobs.

She raised her concerns to the managers, but they minimized the issue for months. One of the managers introduced a quick fix that didn't actually fix the problem. I teamed up with her to dig a bit deeper and we gathered compelling evidence that the experimental results were botched and the consequences could be really bad. Even then, the managers still insisted on using the botched experimental results somehow. My colleague bravely refused, saying the only thing we could do with the results was to "throw them out."

We started the experiments from scratch but doing things

right this time. We had to wait a couple of months to collect new results and see whether our team's AI was indeed bringing monetary value. During this delicate time, the managers kept hiring more people for the team, continuing its explosive growth despite not knowing for sure whether the product worked as expected. I'm pretty sure the people higher up on the ladder never knew what was going on.

Luckily, the new results showed that the AI product was bringing in a lot of revenue, albeit not as much as we initially thought. So, everything was okay in the end, but it could have gone either way. I got the impression that, had things gone badly, telling the truth wouldn't have been the preferred course of action.

Stage 5: Silent burst

The explosive growth of AI teams propped up by questionable validation processes can quite possibly drag on for a few years. However, sooner or later, the organization realizes that there wasn't much bang for the AI buck after all. But it'd be quite humiliating to admit it, especially after advertising the groundbreaking impact of AI to everyone else in the company and the outside world.

So, the most common outcome is a silent implosion. For example, a company discussed in this chapter decided to stop any new development by one of its unsuccessful AI teams and only let them focus on maintaining what they had already created. This rather unfulfilling task resulted in half of the team employees resigning within a year, including the team leader and the one who succeeded him.

In the case of the mini-Theranos I talked about before, the company decided not to devote any budget over the following year to integrate the shady product with the rest of the software, which was a stealthy way of letting the project fall into oblivion. Our team leader still made us write extensive documentation on the product so that it looked like we'd done something important, in case someone cared to look down the line.

Another common outcome is to pivot away from AI. A successful start-up I know, for instance, ended up bringing a great solution to the intended market but without the use of AI.

These aren't the stories that make it to the headlines; only winners prevail in what's known as survivorship bias. The AI hype is thus perpetuated.

What we can do about it

There are a few things we can do to prevent AI projects from suffering the unfortunate fate described above. One thing I often recommend is to tackle an AI project following the *engineering design process.*[55] This process requires engineers to start by first understanding and clearly formulating the client's problem without introducing any biases about the solution. For instance, a problem statement like "Our start-up needs to build an AI system to do X" isn't formulated in the best way, as it mixes the problem with the solution. A better formulation would be "Our clients are struggling with X" (and we should make an effort to truly understand X and describe it in detail). This way, we avoid putting the cart before the horse (Stage 1 from the beginning of this chapter).

If we eventually decide that AI is indeed the best solution to the stated problem, we don't want to unknowingly end up building a faulty solution, as sometimes happens (Stage 2 from above). The most important way to avoid this is to implement a solid validation process to assess machine learning models; this way, we can catch errors early on if they happen. The validation process should be designed and carried out carefully, reminding us of a (properly conducted) clinical trial for a new drug (we'll talk more about validation, and how it's sometimes manipulated, in the next chapter). Another great way to prevent building faulty AI is to study common mistakes and why they happen. Some mistakes, like data leakage, happen quite often in a cookie-cutter way, so it would be great to include them in the machine learning curriculum.

The next stage, in which AI teams grow at an unjustified rate (Stage 3), is also quite preventable. One way to avoid that is to adopt the popular *lean start-up* principle.[56] In a lean start-up, we first build a simple version of a product, the smallest yet usable product we can imagine, and validate it with users. Only after we collect user feedback do we decide which features to develop next. The process is repeated, incrementally building the product and validating it feature after feature. Similarly, we can grow an AI product—and its team—incrementally, validating its benefits at each step, instead of going all in at the start.

When it comes to preventing problems of dishonesty about AI's performance (Stage 4), my best guess is that this comes down to fostering the right work culture. Entrepreneur Ben Horowitz says that work culture isn't bringing dogs to work or having yoga classes in the office; those are perks.[57] Instead, Horowitz says, work culture is a set of core values that specifically help attain business goals. In the case of engineers working with AI, the ideal work culture would welcome admitting mistakes. It would also welcome acknowledging when AI may not be performing as well as expected, and it would allow employees to dump the results of a botched experiment and start over. Those values would put a company in a better place to ultimately succeed in an AI project.

Finally, if things get so bad that a company reaches the last stage, when projects implode but no one finds out (Stage 5), one thing people could do is share their experience with others more openly, maybe in the form of blog articles, white papers, conference presentations and even watercooler conversations. I'm aware this may be a lot to ask—too often the stories of unsuccessful AI projects are swept under the rug, as telling them doesn't bring immediate benefits to a business. I've tried to do my bit in this chapter, by sharing with you some of the untold stories of AI, and I'm hoping that my earlier advice can help some companies interrupt this vicious circle sooner and there will be fewer cases of silent implosion in the future.

Chapter 5

RESEARCH

The innovative methodologies behind AI are usually invented in research labs, where career scientists come up with new techniques and share them with the world in the form of scientific articles published in journals and presented at conferences.

After finishing my early studies, I decided to join the world of scientific research by doing a PhD. I was told I'd be contributing to the advancement of knowledge—a task that I considered highly honorable. However, while the research world allowed me to meet some really inspirational people, it was also quite disappointing.

I soon discovered that AI researchers often follow less-than-pristine practices. Using tricks to exaggerate and manipulate results is worryingly common, and these tricks are often taught to others within research circles behind the scenes.

In this chapter, we'll see how AI research is sometimes not conducted in the most upstanding or rigorous way. We'll examine the reasons why, unfortunately, when a researcher promotes a great AI advancement, you might need to take it with a pinch of salt.

How to prevent cheating

It's possible to study for an exam by memorizing the correct answers to questions found on previous exams instead of learning the content of the class. If the teacher always asks the same questions, you could easily pass the test without ever really learning the material.

That is also a problem in machine learning. Suppose a researcher created a fake machine learning model that memorized the label assigned to each image in a dataset ("image 1 is a strawberry," "image 2 is an airplane," and so on). This model would achieve 100% performance at categorizing the images from the dataset. But the model hasn't learned anything useful.

To prevent that sort of cheating on the test, the AI community always uses *other* data to assess the performance of a model, data that wasn't used for learning. For example, 10% of the images in a dataset may be held back and put in a secret vault before starting to build the model. At the end, the model is evaluated using the unseen images. This is the same reason why teachers won't let students see an exam's questions in advance. This process helps researchers simulate what would happen when a model processes new, unseen data, which is what models are really built for.

Researchers tend to use publicly available datasets to build models, measure their performance and report their results. By using the exact same data, researchers can compare one another's models on an apple-to-apple basis.

Sometimes, researchers agree to exclude a certain portion of the data when building models, pretending like it doesn't exist so they can later use it for fair evaluation. In other, stricter cases, the creators of the dataset keep a portion of data completely hidden from the public, and they use this secret data to independently evaluate the models submitted by researchers.

In theory, this is a fair way of evaluating the performance of machine learning models. In practice, things aren't as pristine as they seem....

How to cheat anyway

Let me tell you a story of how AI's apparent performance can be distorted. A few years ago, I organized a machine learning contest, which is a rather popular activity among researchers. In this type of event, the organizer shares a dataset publicly with the research community and introduces a challenge to be solved using that dataset. In my case, I shared hundreds of square miles of aerial images taken over cities, together with labels indicating where buildings were located in those images. The challenge was to create a machine learning model capable of taking new images and identifying the buildings contained in them. Since buildings look very different around the world, this isn't an easy task.

The researchers submitted their work to me by email, and I used held-out data that the researchers couldn't see to verify their models' performance. From this secret data, I calculated a performance metric indicating how good the model was at identifying buildings. I then displayed the metric, together with the researchers' names, on a leaderboard on the contest's website.

But I made a huge mistake: I left the contest open-ended. I kept accepting submissions and placing them on the leaderboard as they came. That was a rather naïve thing to do on my end.

Soon, researchers started to submit many results instead of just one. They would build a few variants of a model, submit them, check out their performances on the leaderboard, then pick the best-performing model, tweak it to create many variants, submit results again, and so on. A team from a university submitted 60 different results to the contest. Other researchers, many of them from reputable institutions, submitted a dozen models or more. Afterward, they would select the best figure to publicize their model's performance and claim that they'd pushed the boundaries of AI.

The practice of weeding out bad results as if they didn't

exist and reporting only the best ones is informally known as *cherry-picking*. At first sight, cherry-picking might seem like a good idea—after all, what is wrong with picking the best results? But there's a catch.

Imagine being allowed to take an exam many times, pick the highest grade you obtained and report that figure as your overall grade. Even if you answered questions at random, chances are you would get a good grade in one of your attempts and you'd be able to pass the exam. So, the cherry-picking process makes it seem like you know your stuff better than you do.

Your apparent performance can be distorted even more by doing cherry-picking repeatedly. Suppose you take the exam again a few times (let's assume the teacher doesn't change the questions, just like I didn't change the evaluation images in my contest). In these new attempts you answer the questions by slightly varying the answers in the highest-scoring exam from the previous round. Some of these random variations of your answers will probably score even higher than before, so when you cherry-pick the best one, you increase your apparent performance even more. By repeating this process, you could soon get a perfect score without ever learning anything.

The same goes for machine learning. If we create, say, 60 different models, pick the one that scores highest on the dataset used to evaluate it, tweak it to produce many new variations of the model, pick the best one again according to that same dataset, and so on, we end up with a model that works better and better on the dataset used to evaluate it. But we lose sight of whether the improvement is genuine or due to just refining a model by brute force so that it works well only on the data used to evaluate it.

The problem with cherry-picking is in assuming that the resulting performance is *general,* meaning that the model has really learned and will work well with data other than the one it was repeatedly evaluated on. If we engage in severe cherry-picking, we may be badly surprised when we use the model in real life later on—with new images or sentences never encountered before—as the performance drops sharply.

If you remember, the idea of using a separate dataset for evaluation, keeping it in a secret vault, was not to "peek" into the correct answers when building a model. But cherry-picking is just that—we peek into the correct answers to guide our work. That's why, ideally, we should only use the evaluation data once. Every time we select and improve models after evaluating them, we need to use some new data in a new evaluation round, just like a teacher changes the exam's questions each time.

Had I been aware of how cherry-picking can distort results, I would have only accepted submissions to my contest up to a certain date and only revealed the leaderboard to everyone simultaneously, at the end, just once. I don't know whether the participants of the contest that submitted dozens of models were intentionally trying to inflate their performance. Maybe, just like myself when I designed the contest, they weren't aware that cherry-picking could have this effect. But who knows.

Unfortunately, while contests are organized and controlled, most research in AI does not happen that way. In most cases, researchers decide for themselves how to evaluate their models, so they can cherry-pick without consequences. A study analyzing 27 scientific articles about machine learning used in finance to forecast equity prices revealed that in 15 out of those 27 articles, the researchers had built many different models and cherry-picked the one with the highest performance.[58] In half of the cases, the researchers had created at least five different models before cherry-picking the best one, and some had created as many as 70.

In some problem areas, researchers sometimes use the same dataset repeatedly for several years to evaluate their models, which they continuously refine, without ever evaluating them using new data. They keep claiming to advance the capabilities of machine learning in general, but sometimes it's hard to see whether they've just come up with a model that gets a good score when measured using one specific dataset and nothing else.

Another common practice among researchers is to compare the performance of their models against that of other models developed by other authors. This is meant to put their proposed models in perspective, but can we trust this process to accurately show how well a model performs? If you look at most scientific articles in machine learning, you will see something like this at the end:

	Dataset 1	Dataset 2	Dataset 3
Author's model	**97%**	**87%**	95%
Competitor A's model	95%	82%	**96%**
Competitor B's model	96%	79%	87%
Competitor C's model	89%	81%	85%

In this kind of table, the authors report the performance of different machine learning models in some numerical terms—say, the percentage of images categorized correctly. They compare their own model with other models, all evaluated on multiple datasets. The best performance per dataset is highlighted in boldface. The model presented by the authors is always the one that scored the most boldfaced numbers, and so the authors claim not just that their model outperforms some competitors on some data but that their research pushes the boundaries of AI overall.

But how can we be sure that the results aren't cherry-picked and that there weren't many other instances where the author's own model didn't perform as well that they chose not to report?

My experience from working in research tells me that cherry-picking is, unfortunately, very common in these comparisons. Researchers often carefully choose the datasets that prove what they want to prove—that their model is the best among competitors—and don't report less favorable results on other datasets. They can also choose which other models to compare theirs against, so they often pick the ones they beat and ignore the ones that outperform theirs.

This practice is problematic when we rely on the comparisons to conclude that a model is great overall, and thus the computer is becoming smarter by the day, when, in reality, the model has proven not to work that well in some other, concealed cases. It's as if a hotel claimed that its Tripadvisor rating kept improving every year but reached that conclusion by analyzing good reviews only.

I've even heard senior researchers teach tricks for cherry-picking results in a graceful way. For instance, they say you should always use at least two well-known public datasets in the comparisons to make your research seem credible, even if you ignore other datasets for which the model didn't work. They also say you should always compare the proposed model with at least a handful of the most famous models in the field to build credibility, even if you pretend that other models that scored better than yours didn't exist. You should still always claim—they say—that you "outperformed the state of the art."

A senior researcher once told me to always include a "humblebrag" at the end of an article. In this humblebrag, I would discuss the "limitations" of my methodology, but I should pick a limitation that wasn't too bad. That way, I'd look humble and unbiased while still making my model appear to be pushing the boundaries of AI. I once attended a reputed conference and, in one of the talks, the presenter displayed on her slides a couple of failure cases of her image categorization model. One was a doodle of a fan being mistaken for a windmill, and the other one was a doodle of a guitar mistaken for a violin. A cynical audience member asked if we could see "real failures," but the presenter didn't have any other examples to share.

The high prevalence of cherry-picking has created an artificial "race to the top." Every article seems to prove that AI is getting better and better, but this doesn't always reflect real improvements.

Attention seeking

An important part of researchers' work is to sell their research within academia and to the rest of the world. After all, researchers live off grants, so they need to promote their work to obtain funding and even make the research field look important.

In 2014, the University of Reading organized a Turing test competition. In this competition, researchers could submit their chatbots for evaluation. If a chatbot fooled humans into believing that it was a real person, then it would be the first machine ever to pass the Turing test. Fluent conversation is one of the hardest tasks in AI, so many have considered this the ultimate test for artificial intelligence.

One of the participants, a chatbot called Eugene Goostman, won the competition. The University of Reading published an announcement entitled "Turing test success marks milestone in computing history." The event was highly publicized around the world.

But this result and the methodology were questionable. The organizers of the competition considered the test passed if the machine fooled one third of evaluators, meaning that it would still pass if two thirds were not fooled. Also, evaluators were only allowed to have five-minute conversations with the chatbot. It turns out that Eugene Goostman answered questions in an evasive way and would have probably been unmasked under a more thorough evaluation. Have a look at a conversation between Goostman and computer scientist Scott Aaronson:[59]

Scott: Which is bigger, a shoebox or Mount Everest?

Goostman: I can't make a choice right now. I should think it out later. And I forgot to ask you where you are from...

Scott: How many legs does a camel have?

Goostman: Something between 2 and 4. Maybe, three? :-)))
By the way, I still don't know your specialty—or, possibly, I've missed it?

It is quite clear that the Turing test wasn't passed, but the university and the AI field received a lot of press around the fake milestone.

These publicity stunts are all too common in AI. In 2021, for instance, the University of Exeter published a news article stating that they'd used AI to detect dementia with 92% accuracy.[60] Impressed by this figure, the *Daily Mail* published an article entitled, "Artificial intelligence can now predict who will develop DEMENTIA with 92% accuracy, breakthrough study reveals."

But let's dig a bit deeper.

The *accuracy* is the proportion of correct predictions made by a model. So, in this case, the model made correct predictions 92% of the time. This figure was calculated by comparing the predictions of the model with the real diagnoses of patients who attended a memory clinic.

In this clinic, 10% of clients were diagnosed with dementia. So, imagine you create a fake "AI" model that *always* predicts that a patient does *not* have dementia. This model would reach an accuracy of 90% because it would make the right prediction 90% of the time. So, the 92% figure is not that impressive when we consider that 90% accuracy can be attained by doing nothing at all.

In the original article, the researchers of this dementia-detecting AI reported other metrics that are more meaningful, instead of just the accuracy.[61] For example, they reported that their model had a sensitivity of 45%, which means that it correctly identified 45% of people who really had dementia. This number doesn't sound that great, so, in the news article, the university only reported the less meaningful but more impressive 92% figure.

Another popular claim among researchers seeking to impress others is that their models "beat humans." For instance, a team from Microsoft Researchers claimed that their model for image categorization was the first one to surpass human-level performance at that task.[62] To base this claim, researchers must compare the performance of their models against some calculation of human performance.

But the calculation of human performance is often done in a dubious way. And in many cases, researchers omit from their articles key information about how they calculated human performance,[63] including the number of human participants studied, the recruitment method for the participants, a measure of how much they disagree on the labels, and their level of expertise at the task. In the Microsoft Research article mentioned above, the authors simply borrowed the human-level performance figure from another article. The figure from the other article was calculated by asking a single person to manually label 1,500 images, without indicating this person's background, abilities or circumstances in detail. This process raises many questions. For instance, how do we account for human fatigue? If I'm asked to manually label 1,500 images into categories, I'm likely to do a poor job because I'm tired or bored. Visual acuity could also affect a human's performance at this task.

Moreover, as we discussed in Chapter 3, just counting how often mistakes are made is not a sure way to prove that the machine beats the human. What about the gravity of mistakes?

When I worked in research, I was guilty of attention-seeking behavior myself. Remember I mentioned above that I once organized a machine learning contest (to which some researchers submitted 60 models). The very reason I launched the contest was to gain attention, as people from the research world had told me that launching a contest and describing it in an article was a sure way to gain publicity. Contest participants would end up citing my article in their own articles, thus making my research and the topic look relevant. Some people even advised me to kick off the contest by submitting my own set of results, but I should secretly submit mediocre results on purpose. This way, researchers would easily be able to beat my results and thus would be encouraged to submit their own.

This attention-seeking behavior is beneficial to researchers. The system incentivizes them to sell (and sometimes oversell) the value and accomplishments of AI, creating the massive hype we've seen in previous chapters. However, one of its dire consequences is that the public and even researchers themselves end up having an overly optimistic idea of the advancements in AI.

Chapter 6

THE MIND

In 2022, news went viral of a Google engineer, Blake Lemoine, who claimed that a chatbot developed by Google, called LaMDA, had become conscious. Blake Lemoine was suspended and fired soon after. "I know a person when I talk to it," Lemoine told the *Washington Post*. "It doesn't matter whether they have a brain made of meat in their head. Or if they have a billion lines of code. I talk to them. And I hear what they have to say, and that is how I decide what is and isn't a person."[64]

In a blog article, Lemoine said, "Over the course of the past six months LaMDA has been incredibly consistent in its communications about what it wants and what it believes its rights are as a person." He also said he'd taught meditation to LaMDA before his suspension and that he hoped "it's keeping up its daily meditation routine without me there to guide it."[65]

The debate on AI's consciousness isn't new, but this event reinvigorated the discussion. This chapter, if you'll allow me, will be more speculative and philosophical than the previous ones. We will discuss two related topics that have been in the spotlight of AI debate for decades. First, we'll discuss whether AI can be conscious. Second, we'll discuss whether it's possible in principle to build computers that can do anything a human can do.

What do we know about the brain?

The brain's processing is performed by electrically excitable cells called neurons. Each neuron receives input signals from many other neurons through filaments known as dendrites. Each neuron then produces a single output, which is passed on to other neurons through a filament called the axon:

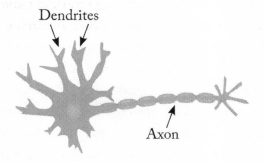

Dendrites

Axon

But do we really understand neurons? Do we know what a neuron exactly does, how it produces an output from its inputs?

Over the past few years, there has grown to be an increasing body of material that gives the impression that we already understand how neurons and the overall brain work. In the words of neuroscientist Daniel Graham,[66] "It's easy to get the impression that science has by now achieved a very good understanding of how brains work. The onslaught of popular articles and books that aim to explain the workings of our brain, as well as the proliferation of the prefix neuro in other fields from economics to marketing to art history, can give the impression that neuroscience is a solved problem and that the answers neuroscientists have discovered can guide other fields."

There is a popular model to explain neurons that says that a neuron calculates a sum of its inputs. If this sum exceeds a certain threshold, then the neuron fires an output signal; otherwise, it doesn't fire. The strength of the connection between neurons may change through time, so some inputs contribute more to the sum than others. According to this model, learning is achieved by altering the strength of the connections between neurons, which affects the ultimate value of the sums.

This simple model of neuron behavior has been referenced a lot within AI. There is a type of machine learning template, called an artificial neural network, which uses this simple neuron model. Instead of using rules of the type "If some input < some value" as we saw in Chapter 1, it uses rules of the type "If weighted sum of inputs > some value".

In 1997, futurist Ray Kurzweil used this model of neurons to estimate the processing power of the brain and famously predicted that electronic computers would reach this power between 2015 and 2025. The required processing power has indeed been reached. But was the model of neurons used to calculate the brain's power correct?

In reality, actual biological neurons are much more complicated that the popular sum-and-threshold model. For instance, when a neuron fires, it actually emits a quick succession of several pulses rather than sending one single signal. And when it is not firing, it is actually still firing, albeit at a slower rate.[67] Over the years, much more complicated models have been developed to try to explain how neurons work. However, these models still cannot predict what scientists observe when studying the workings of real neurons. For example, in 2017, a group of researchers discovered through experiments that neurons are likely to contain many independent units inside them that perform many sum-and-threshold operations, as opposed to just one.[68] And, in 2020, another group of researchers discovered that the dendrites themselves carry out complicated computations;[69] they aren't just "wires" that carry signals as we previously thought. To complicate things even more, the fluid that surrounds neurons contains molecules, known as neuromodulators, which affect neurons' behavior in a way that isn't fully understood. So, while progress has been made, our understanding of neurons and brains is still quite poor.

Some people have engaged in remarkable initiatives to try to understand the brain. In 2009, neuroscientist Henry Markram announced at a TED conference that he'd soon be simulating the entire human brain in a computer. "We can do it within 10 years, and if we do succeed, we will send to TED, in 10 years, a hologram to talk to you." The European Union awarded—brace yourself—one billion euros to this initiative.

But it soon became clear that this project wouldn't succeed in simulating the brain. Markram was asked to step down two years into the project. The goals ended up being adjusted to much smaller promises, and no one has yet sent a hologram to do a TED talk.

As of today, the brain of only one organism has been fully mapped out, meaning that researchers could create a map of all connections between neurons, or *connectome*. The organism is a tiny worm called C. Elegans, which has around 300 neurons and 7,000 connections among them. However, it was impossible to simulate the observed worm's behavior from the map, as it just tells us which neurons are connected to which but not exactly how they work. In the words of neuroscientist Anthony Movshon, "Our understanding of the worm has not been materially enhanced by having that connectome available to us. We don't have a comprehensive model of how the worm's nervous system actually produces the behaviors. What we have is a sort of a bed on which we can build experiments—and many people have built many elegant experiments on that bed. But that connectome by itself has not explained anything."[70] So, the wiring diagram of C. Elegans might be useful for future research, but it hasn't helped us understand how brains work in detail, much less how human brains work. Our current knowledge about brains is still very far from letting us build an artificial brain with computers.

What do we know about consciousness?

Consciousness is the phenomenon of experiencing things, of being sentient. Right now, for instance, you are experiencing what it's like to read this text. You can see letters on the page and also observe other stuff through your peripheral vision. You also experience thoughts; if you close your eyes, you can mentally hum a song and experience in your head what it's like to listen to music. When you're under general anesthesia, you're unconscious. You're also unconscious when you fall asleep until you start dreaming.

Our understanding of consciousness in the brain is still quite poor. We do know that some parts of the brain are in charge of unconscious actions (like controlling heartbeat) while others process conscious perceptions (like vision), but we don't understand why some parts contribute to our consciousness while others don't. We also don't understand how general anesthesia works; we just know from experience that anesthetics turn off consciousness temporarily, but we don't know the mechanism behind it.

But there's an even deeper question, beyond the mere organization of our brains. The question is: What are the necessary conditions for consciousness to appear in nature? What is the law of nature that defines exactly when and how consciousness emerges from a lump of matter? Is there, for instance, a minimum number of connections that are necessary for a system to become conscious? Or is there a certain material, say, carbon-containing matter, that gives rise to consciousness while others don't? Finding the rules of nature that explain when consciousness emerges from the physical world is known as *the hard problem of consciousness*.[71]

The hard problem of consciousness is hard because it cannot be solved solely through physical laws. For example, stating that a certain configuration of carbon atoms gives rise to a conscious being is not a physical law by itself—it doesn't explain any physical phenomena and probably cannot be tested experimentally. But it would be a law of nature—on top of physics—that would help us better understand the universe we live in.

Because the problem is so hard and beyond the realm of physics, some people have chosen to dodge the question or deem it unimportant. Some people even deny that they are conscious beings themselves. Have a look at the following passage by Jeff Hawkings from his book *On Intelligence*:[72]

The British scientist looked at me. "Of course you are conscious."

"No, I don't think so. I may look that way to you, but I'm not a conscious human being. Don't worry about it, I'm okay with it."

She said, "Well, don't you perceive wonder?" and swept her arm toward the glistening water as the sun began to sink and the sky turned iridescent salmon-pink.

"Yes. I see all this stuff. So?"

"Then how do you explain your subjective experience?"

I replied, "Yes, I know I'm here. I have memories of things like this evening. But I don't feel anything special is going on, so if you feel something special maybe I'm just not conscious."

The hard problem of consciousness remains unsolved and is the subject of much discussion within AI and elsewhere. Some people think that the AI field shouldn't be concerned about consciousness at all. The goal of AI, they argue, should be to build machines with human-level performance at many tasks regardless of whether they're conscious or not. However, creating a conscious machine leads to several ethical dilemmas. Would the machines experience pain or sorrow and, if so, how should we treat them? Can we destroy a robot we created if we know it has become conscious? So, for this and other reasons that we'll see in a minute, the debate of consciousness often makes its way into the AI field.

Would an artificial brain be conscious?

The *computational theory of the mind* says that our brain performs computations just like the computers we use on a daily basis, our smartphones and laptops. The theory asserts that every neuron performs a computation to transform its inputs and produce an output. In other words, every neuron runs a computer program. The product of all these programs run together controls our human function and gives rise to our thoughts. These computer programs could be run on any other device, say, a microchip. So, according to the computational theory of the mind, it is possible to build artificial brains with computers in principle even if it may be hard to do so in practice. Let's assume for a moment that the computational theory is true and see what it tells us about consciousness.

Suppose a friend—let's call him John—lets us tamper with his brain. We replace a single neuron in John's brain with a silicon microchip designed to run the exact same computer program as the original neuron. Since we are assuming that neurons are equivalent to computers, we should be able to do this in principle. (Let's ignore any practical impediments, such as the size or speed of the microchip, which distracts us from the crux of the issue.)

This microchip is inserted inside John's brain where the original neuron used to be, and it's connected to adjacent neurons just like its predecessor. We can now get rid of the original neuron. John's modified brain works exactly the same as his original brain did, as the program hasn't changed.

Suppose we repeat this process, replacing all John's neurons one by one with equivalent microchips, until the whole brain is an electronic circuit. John's new brain is exactly equivalent in functionality to his original one. His behavior is exactly the same as before, as his entire brain's computer program hasn't changed.

Would John be conscious or not? If we say that electronic John isn't conscious, then we must answer at which point he lost his consciousness. When we replaced just one neuron in John's brain, did he become a bit less of a conscious being? Has his consciousness faded away little by little as we replaced neurons one by one, even though his behavior is unchanged and the program running in his brain is the same? Or did the consciousness disappear all of a sudden, say, after 50% of the neurons were replaced by silicon equivalents?

Many people have argued that, while it is conceivable that consciousness could fade away or disappear this way, it is quite implausible.[73] Why would John's brain require neurons to be made of a certain material for his consciousness to emerge? Why would only organic matter produce consciousness and not some other matter running the same computer program? Some have accused that viewpoint of "carbon chauvinism." The computational theory of the mind asserts that consciousness emerges from the act of computation in the brain, regardless of the medium used to run the program. According to this theory, our consciousness arises from software that happens to be running in the currently carbon hardware of our brains. But who knows—and could we ever know? If we asked questions to John, he'd be answering in the exact same way as before, as if his brain hadn't been tampered with; after all, his new brain is functionally equivalent to the original one.

Sci-Fi

The computational theory of the mind leads to some fascinating sci-fi scenarios. Suppose we modify John's brain in a different way. Instead of replacing a neuron with a microchip, we install a device that captures the neurons' inputs and transmits them through a tiny radio transmitter to a person in China. (China has been used repeatedly in this kind of thought exercise before, possibly because of its large population. No offense to the Chinese.)

The person in China has the job of manually calculating the result of running the original neuron's computer program. For this, he can use pen and paper, just like we do when we multiply or divide numbers without a calculator. Once he's finished, the Chinese individual sends the result of the computation back to John's skull, where a device intercepts it and plugs it into the brain where the original neuron's axon used to be. We can now remove the original neuron, which has been fully bypassed, thanks to the help of this Chinese person performing John's calculations for him.

As usual, most people think there's no reason to believe that anything would change in John's conscious experience. After all, a piece of his brain was replaced by a system that produces exactly the same result as before (remember, we're not focusing on the practicality of doing this—let's imagine that the Chinese person works really fast and can send the message back to John's skull in a fraction of a second).

Now, suppose we continue the process by tampering with a second neuron. We now send the signal to another Chinese individual who runs this second neuron's computer program, also using pen and paper. The output of this program is also sent back and plugged into John's skull in the right place. Once again, John is unlikely to notice anything because the program running inside his brain is exactly the same as before.

We keep going, replacing all of John's neurons, one by one. In the end, no biological neurons are left. Again, as this process is performed, there are few reasons to believe that John would lose his consciousness; after all, we replaced his neurons one by one with alternative devices (in this case, Chinese individuals) that do exactly the same job as his neurons did before.

We could also have the Chinese people talk to one another, instead of sending signals individually back and forth to John's skull. We only need to intercept John's sensory inputs, such as his vision, and send them to China. After running the computer programs of all his neurons in China, we collect the motor outputs, such as the ones that move muscles, and plug them into John's nervous system in the right places. John keeps acting like John, but the running of his mental program is fully outsourced.

According to the computational theory of the mind, John would still experience consciousness due to the actions of billions of Chinese people who keep calculating the outputs of running his brain's computer program while talking to one another and taking notes. Some people consider this an obvious observation and aren't baffled by the idea. For others, this is pure sci-fi and defeats our common notion of consciousness and the sense of self.

Now, suppose that we scanned the content of Einstein's brain at some point during his life and wrote down his mental computer program in a very long book. We could open this book years or centuries later and have it answer any question just like Einstein would have.[74] All it would require would be to leaf through the book really fast and follow its instructions to the letter to run the computer program.

Running the computer program by browsing the book and calculating the outputs is indistinguishable as having Einstein's original neurons run the program. So, according to the computational theory, running the program in the book gives rise to Einstein's consciousness. In this regard, physicist Roger Penrose says, "Since the book is supposed to be merely a particular embodiment of the algorithm that constitutes Einstein's 'self', it would actually *be* Einstein."[75] So, it's not that this book just gives us the same answers as Einstein; it would give rise to Einstein's sentient being. After all, the consciousness of the original Einstein existed because that very same computer program was executed.

Many other curious sci-fi scenarios arise from viewing consciousness as the execution of a computer program. For example, you could scan your brain's contents and store them as a back-up or transmit it to other places at high speeds. Computer scientist Scott Aaronson tells us:

> "Planning a dangerous mountain climbing trip? Before you go, make a backup of yourself—or two or three—so that if tragedy should strike, you can restore from backup and then continue life as if you'd never left. Want to visit Mars? Don't bother with the perilous months-long journey through space; just use a brain-scanning machine to 'fax yourself' there as pure information, whereupon another machine on Mars will construct a new body for you, functionally identical to the original."[76]

These scenarios raise philosophical and ethical questions. Aaronson outlines a few for us:

> After you've been faxed to Mars, what should be done with the "original" copy of you left on Earth? Should it be destroyed with a quick, painless gunshot to the head? Would *you* agree to be "faxed" to Mars, knowing that that's what would be done to the original? [...] Likewise, suppose you return unharmed from your mountain-climbing trip, and

decide that the backup copies you made before you left are now an expensive nuisance. If you destroy them, are you guilty of murder? Or is it more like suicide? Or neither?

While these scenarios seem far-fetched, they are a natural consequence of the computational theory of the mind. So, the proponents of the theory should be ready to study them and suggest solutions to these ethical dilemmas. On this matter, Aaronson says that declaring that the mind is a computer program to "escape all that philosophical crazy-talk" is ironically backward, as we end up landing on a swamp of philosophical perplexities rather than dodging them.

Let me mention one last important consequence of the computational theory of the mind. Take a moment now to decide whether to continue reading this book or take a break. (I hope you continue!) The computational theory of the mind says that every decision we make in our minds is completely predictable because it's dictated by a computer program inside our brains (and we can always predict what a computer program will do next). So, if I could take a snapshot of your brain right before you make a decision, I would be able to predict the decision with 100% accuracy. In other words, according to the computational theory of the mind, we do not have free will. Instead, free will is an illusion and we are mere spectators of the decisions made by our brains in a completely predictable way. Some people are okay with this; others find this pill hard to swallow.

Can any computer program become conscious?

When Blake Lemoine asserted that Google's software had become sentient, the software in question was not an exact simulation of the brain; it didn't even intend to imitate brain structure in any way. That is the case with all AI today, which follows machine learning's blank-filling recipe instead of trying to build artificial brains.

We saw that, according to the computational theory of the mind, a full-scale imitation of the brain would likely be conscious. But what about other, less complicated software that we use on a daily basis, which doesn't intend to imitate the brain? Is it conscious too?

The computational theory doesn't have an answer to this. But some people have observed that if running a computer program is what creates consciousness, then we could claim anything running a computer program to be sentient. If Google's AI is conscious, then why isn't a thermostat conscious? After all, it also runs a computer program. David Chalmers argued that thermostats are likely to be conscious, although "we will likely be unable to sympathetically imagine these experiences any better than a blind person can imagine sight, or than a human can imagine what it is like to be a bat."[77]

We can also, for instance, organize obstacles on a billiard table to solve simple mathematical problems. The input is given by the direction in which we shoot a ball. The output is obtained by checking out which pocket the ball lands in. The obstacles around the table are especially arranged to direct the ball to the right pocket and solve the problem correctly. The balls bouncing around effectively run a simple computer program. So, do the balls give rise to a conscious being as they bounce around the table?

Some people have even pointed out that pretty much anything can be seen as executing a computer program. For example, the molecules of water in a bucket bounce around and thus may also execute some form of computation. Is the water in the bucket conscious?

Philosopher John Searle proposed a famous thought experiment that goes as follows: A person who doesn't speak Chinese memorizes a computer program that, given a question, can give a correct answer in Chinese. This person hides in a room, receives questions in Chinese from outside and responds with correct answers based on that program. To the outside world, it seems like there is someone inside the room that consciously understands Chinese. However, the individual answering the questions just follows the instructions in the program and doesn't consciously speak Chinese or understand what's being said. Searle's point is that even if a person produces an output that perfectly imitates the behavior of a conscious being, it doesn't mean this person is equally conscious. Searle would disagree with Google employee Blake Lemoine's statement: "I hear what they have to say, and that is how I decide what is and isn't a person."

But proponents of the computational theory of the mind disagree with Searle. They say that the person inside the room could run a computer program that mimics the brain of a Chinese speaker and that would give rise to a conscious being in the room, just like Einstein's consciousness emerged from leafing through a book containing his brain's computer program. So, there would be a Chinese-speaking conscious being in the room—but it wouldn't be the person running the program, it would be another mysterious conscious being that arises from the act of running the program. But this refutation of Searle's argument still assumes we're exactly imitating an entire brain. What about a simpler computer program that tries to give answers in Chinese but that doesn't seek to imitate the brain? That would describe most AI software today.

The question of whether and how consciousness emerges from computer programs remains unsolved. If Google's AI is conscious, then why wouldn't a thermostat also be conscious? And if Google's AI isn't conscious, then why are our brains conscious?

Why do we care?

As you read the last few paragraphs, you may have nodded along or shaken your head in disbelief. Conscious thermostats? Einstein's consciousness immortalized in a book? No free will? It may sound perfectly acceptable to you or utterly absurd.

Some people are okay with those strange sci-fi scenarios. After all, they argue, we've come to grips with phenomena initially deemed ludicrous, such as light propagating in a vacuum or matter being made of atoms.

Other people see those scenarios as too far-fetched to be taken seriously. In that case, there must be something wrong with the assumptions that led us to them.

For example, accepting the computational theory of the mind leads us directly to the lack of free will—every action you take is programmed in your brain and entirely predictable. If you disagree with that, then you have to reject the premise that led us there; you have to reject that your neurons are equivalent to computers as proposed by the computational theory of the mind.

The computational theory was also the basis of the other sci-fi scenarios given above. We spoke, for instance, of replacing John's neurons one by one with an equivalent computer. But that assumes that neurons are equivalent to computers. So, if you consider the outcomes too far-fetched—like John's consciousness enacted by billions of Chinese people working in tandem—you may want to revise one of the main assumptions leading you there, which is that our neurons are equivalent to computers.

This debate is important for analyzing the future of AI. The idea that our minds are computers is the ultimate argument supporting that artificial general intelligence is possible; all it takes is to scan a brain and use it as a template to build an equivalent computer. Philosopher Nick Bostrom writes, "The availability of the brain as template provides strong support for the claim that machine intelligence is ultimately feasible [...] Intelligent software would be produced by scanning and closely modeling the computational structure of a biological brain."[78] So, according to this argument, since our minds are just computers, it is, in principle, possible to someday build computers that can do anything a human can do (but it could take a while).

If you reject the computational theory of the mind because of its strange implications on consciousness, free will, or something else, then we lose that strong argument in favor of the feasibility of artificial general intelligence. If our minds are something more than just large carbon-based implementations of ordinary computers, then we can't guarantee that a computer will ever be able to exactly imitate what a brain does and thus attain our level of intelligence at every task.

Some people accept that minds are computers, thus accepting the sci-fi baggage that comes with it, and celebrate that artificial general intelligence is possible in principle. Other people, such as physicist Roger Penrose,[79] reject the idea that our minds are computers. This makes the sci-fi scenarios mentioned above irrelevant and leads to the rejection of the idea that artificial general intelligence can be realized with computers as we know them today.

The debate is still ongoing.

Are our brains fundamentally smarter than computers?

Suppose we reject the computational theory of the mind. This alleviates the ethical and existential pain that comes with it, like conscious thermostats and copies of your mental computer program sent to Mars.

But now we face another painful question—if the mind isn't a computer, then what is it? What could possibly be happening physically inside a brain that a computer would not be able to imitate? For that to be the case, there must be something that a computer *cannot* do that a brain can. Let's explore four possibilities.

Randomness

Computers follow instructions to the letter, so everything they do is predictable. Even when a computer generates a sequence of apparently random numbers, for instance, in an online casino, the sequence of numbers is totally predictable if you know the inputs and the program. Of course, an online casino makes sure you don't have access to that information, so the numbers that come up are effectively unpredictable and appear random to you, but it is fully predictable if you have access to the right information.

But it's likely that the physical universe isn't entirely predictable. Quantum theory—the current physical theory used to predict the behavior of microscopic particles—asserts that particles sometimes behave in a *truly* random and thus completely unpredictable way (even though this is still debated). If true randomness indeed exists, then generating truly random data may be one thing our brains can do that computers can't.

The question is, even if our brains are capable of true randomness—which makes us different from computers—would that give us the power to be more intelligent than computers, that is, to solve problems that computers can't solve? Many people are skeptical about this. Physicist Roger Penrose tells us, "It is hard to see what advantage there might be in having a *genuinely* random input, as opposed to a merely *pseudo-random* one that *can* be generated entirely computationally."[80]

It is worth noting that (fake) randomness is very important in machine learning. When the machine learns, it usually tries out many chaotically selected ways of filling in the blanks in the model to see if one of them improves the outcome by chance. The options aren't truly random, as they are predictable, but they are quite chaotic in order to let the machine explore a wide variety of options. But would the machine learn better if it could explore truly random options as opposed to chaotic options? Most people don't see how.

Even if randomness could give our brains more problem-solving power than computers, then we could equip a computer with that power; all it takes is to plug in a device that generates truly random numbers by measuring quantum properties of particles, and then the computer uses those truly random numbers as inputs. Devices like this already exist and even come in the form of USB sticks.

So, while many people don't see how true randomness could give us an advantage over computers, this fundamental difference is worth noting.

Precision

The computer invented by Alan Turing in 1936 and all computers we use today are *digital.* This means that they store data and take inputs and outputs as sequences of digits, such as numbers or letters. Today's computers use two different digits for this purpose—0 and 1, also known as binary. So, everything in a computer is expressed as a sequence of binary numbers. Images, for example, are comprised of a collection of pixels, and each pixel takes an integer value from 0 to 255—or 00000000 to 11111111 in binary.

Being digital makes computers highly robust, as it's easy to distinguish digits from one another. For instance, 0 is represented by a low voltage in an electronic circuit and 1 by a high voltage, which is unambiguous, compared to trying to use finer voltage values like 13.456 to represent precise numbers. The thing is, a number like pi, which has an infinite number of digits (3.141592…), has to be truncated and converted into a finite number of binary digits. Some precision is always lost in this process.

In contrast, brains aren't digital—they aren't bound to representing data as sequences of digits. This is another major difference between brains and computers. It is thus conceivable that if we replace a neuron with a digital computer, the fake neuron will lose too much precision and will thus never be able to recreate the behavior of the real neuron. As observed by philosopher David Chalmers, "It is true that a system with unlimited precision might have cognitive capacities that no digital system could ever have."[81] However, as Chalmer notes, the brain is a hot and messy place where precision is hard to maintain. So, for a lot of people, it is hard to imagine that our brain function could rely on extremely precise data.

So, once again, there is a difference between brains and computers, but many people are skeptical that this difference could empower us with capabilities that computers don't have. But who knows.

Copiability

Another stellar difference between brains and computers is that a brain's state cannot be copied exactly. Computer programs and the internal state of a computer can always be copied; that's why, if brains are computers, we could allegedly immortalize Einstein's consciousness in a book by peeking into his brain and transcribing everything.

However, quantum theory tells us that microscopic particles have certain properties that cannot be copied—the moment we probe into them, we alter them in an irreversible way. So, if we try to make a copy of Einstein's brain, we necessarily lose—and destroy—some fine-grained details of his brain's state. But are these irretrievable fine-grained details important to consciousness or intelligence? No one knows for sure.

Scott Aaronson points out that the impossibility of copying the fine-grained details of matter may answer some of the sci-fi scenarios described above. For example, we can't carbon-copy Einstein's brain down to the smallest detail without altering some physical aspects of his original brain. And we can't send a copy of your brain's content to Mars down to the smallest detail without changing it.

This may also shed some light into the free-will debate. If I peek into your brain to try to predict what you'll do next, I will necessarily alter the state of your brain. So, if your actions depended on the fine-grained details that I inevitably wiped out, I could never know what you would really have done next had I not intervened.

Computationally unsolvable problems

Computers solve problems by performing simple operations one by one following the instructions specified in a program. Each instruction tells the computer how to map combinations of inputs and memory contents to outputs and possibly update the memory with new data. This process, *computation,* might seem really simple, but long programs, large memories, and fast processing speeds make it very powerful; it is responsible for the sophisticated functionality of today's computers. However, we know of some problems that computation *cannot* solve. In fact, the field of computer science itself started around that. In 1936, Alan Turing wrote an article with the first description ever of a general-purpose digital computer, together with an example of a problem it couldn't solve.[82]

Have a look at the following shape:

Do you think tiles with that shape could be used to tile a floor of any size?

I'm pretty sure you answered "yes." You immediately saw how these pieces can be fit together indefinitely:

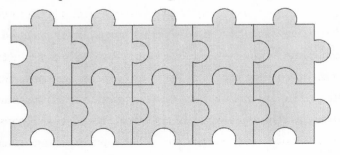

We're all familiar with the idea of such tiling patterns re-peated infinitely. We've seen them, for instance, in honey-combs, which bees construct by intertwining hexagonal cells. We also find zigzag tiling in parquet floors—forming her-ringbones or chevrons—and in mosaics.

Now, consider a regular pentagon:

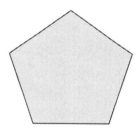

Can you picture whether it's possible to tile a floor with this shape without leaving any gaps? Try it!

Something doesn't quite add up, right? It seems that whichever way you put two pentagons together, the result-ing space around them is too awkwardly shaped to snugly fit another one. Indeed, it is impossible to tile a floor using pentagons without leaving gaps.

The problem of determining whether you can tile a floor of any size with a given set of tile shapes is known to be com-putationally unsolvable.[83] This means that it is impossible to write a computer program that gives the correct answer for any input tile shapes. We can write a program to calculate an answer to individual cases (jigsaw puzzles, regular polygons, herringbones, etc.), but we can't write a program that gives the correct answer for all possible shapes. This is an example of a list of many problems known to be computationally unsolvable. (Some people have even argued that this shows that we can always find, for certain problems, new inputs whose solution we as humans can know but that a program can't, and that this proves that our minds are more than computers[84]—but this conclusion has been disputed and is the source of a lot of debate.[85])

So, here's a thought: What if our brains perform some physical process that hasn't been discovered yet, which lets us solve computationally unsolvable problems like the tiling problem mentioned above? Sometimes we get the impression that physics is "finished," that we already understand all the physical laws that govern the universe. But that's really not the case. While advances in physics have helped us make impressive progress in medicine and build GPS satellites and microchips, what we know now is far from a complete account of the laws of the universe.

Quantum theory, which explains the behavior of microscopic particles, is currently formulated in a rather dissatisfying way, and thus many people agree we haven't gotten to the real answer yet. A problematic aspect of quantum theory is that it states that particles behave in a strange way when *we're not looking at them* and behave in a familiar way when we do look. For instance, so long as we're not looking, a particle can be in many places at once. But then the moment we look—or, more technically, the moment we make a *measurement*—that weird behavior disappears and the particle is found to be in only one place. The theory works well to calculate a probability for each possible outcome of a measurement in the lab, but many people argue that it doesn't explain reality.

Philosopher of science Tim Maudlin tells us,

> A precisely defined physical theory would never use terms like 'observation,' 'measurement,' 'system' or 'apparatus' in its fundamental postulates. It would instead say precisely *what exists* and *how it behaves*. If the description is correct, then the theory would account for the outcomes of all experiments, since experiments contain existing things that behave somehow.[86]

As if quantum theory didn't already have enough problems, there is another elephant in the room. Quantum theory leaves one remarkable interaction of nature completely unexplained: gravity. Since gravity is rather weak at the scale of particles, it doesn't affect the results of experiments in the lab. A comprehensive theory of particles should account for gravity, but the current best theory doesn't.

Instead, gravity is explained by a separate theory, Einstein's general theory of relativity. This theory is, unfortunately, incompatible with quantum theory; quantum theory does not account for the most important tenets of general relativity, while general relativity does not account for the most important tenets of quantum theory. So, either quantum theory or the general theory of relativity, or both, will have to change at some point. No one knows how.

To top it all off, the general theory of relativity may also have problems of its own. This theory is used to explain the motion of large objects like satellites and planets. However, its predictions don't match the motion of celestial bodies at larger scale, such as the rotation of some galaxies or the expansion of the universe as a whole. If we want general relativity to hold up and make the right predictions, we must assume that there is a vast amount of energy out there that we know little about, and also a vast amount of invisible matter, different from any matter known until now.

Calculations show that, for general relativity to hold up, the missing stuff, called *dark matter* and *dark energy,* must amount to a whopping 95% of all matter and energy in the universe. So, there are two options here: either general relativity is wrong or current physics only understands 5% of the stuff out there while the rest is made up of something we don't know. Neither option is flattering for physics.

This all goes to show that our current understanding of physics is incomplete. Most people agree that there will be, at some point, fundamental changes in the field. What if, once we understand physics better, we find physical processes performed by our brains that computers cannot recreate?

Nobel-laureate physicist Roger Penrose believes that there are as-yet-unknown physical processes inside the brain that we will only understand once a new theory of physics is developed. He thinks these special physical processes help us solve mathematical problems that computers can't solve, such as, maybe, the infinite tiling problem we discussed above. If this is the case, these processes give us more intelligence than could ever be attained by digital computers.

If and when

There is a popular view that holds that artificial general intelligence "is not a question of if but when." In this view, the "if" question isn't up for discussion—it's assumed that AGI can be attained. We can see this view in many headlines about AI: "What will our society look like when artificial intelligence is everywhere?"[87] "What will superintelligent AI be capable of doing?"[88] Examples abound.

We can see a stellar instance of this view in the book *Human Compatible* by Stuart Russell. In this book, Russell mentions a group of researchers that announced that they don't think human-level AI is possible. To this, he comments, "This is the first time serious AI researchers have publicly espoused the view that human-level or superhuman AI is impossible... It's as if a group of leading cancer biologists announced that they had been fooling us all along: they've always known that there will never be a cure for cancer."[89] This view implies that you can only conduct serious AI research if you believe that the answer to the "if" question is "yes."

But as we've seen in this chapter, that "if" question hasn't been answered yet. It is not a universally accepted truth that brains are computers, that artificial general intelligence is possible or that these highly intelligent computers would be conscious. The "if" question has stimulated discussion for years across multiple fields, including biology, philosophy and physics.

I can't provide my own answer to "if" because, as seen in this chapter, it's quite complicated. I do have an answer to the "when" question though: not anytime soon.

CONCLUSION AND PREDICTIONS

Artificial intelligence is not the first remarkable development in history that was rife with high expectations and craze. For over 30 years, the physics community focused significant efforts in the development of *string theory*. This theory soared as a promising candidate to solve one of the greatest unsolved problems in physics—the unification of quantum theory with Einstein's theory of gravity.

Unfortunately, string theory became a dogma. Unlike other physical theories, string theory couldn't be validated or falsified through experiments. So, researchers judged it in subjective ways, using fuzzy criteria such as mathematical beauty. Researchers continued working on this untestable theory for decades, during which time string theory absorbed the majority of the efforts—and funding—in theoretical physics. It soon became hard to find a job in theoretical physics in anything other than string theory.

But as years went by, many weaknesses in the formulation of the theory were discovered. Instead of considering that the very foundations of the theory may be inadequate, physicists started to patch it up and plug its holes. When new problems were discovered, it was patched up again, and then the patches themselves were patched.

Questioning the theory and pursuing other avenues of research was not well received by the community—some said it was career suicide. A sort of sectarianism also appeared. Looking back into that era, physicist Lee Smolin wrote a list of quirks about the string theory community,[90] including the following:

- "A tendency to interpret evidence optimistically, to believe exaggerated or incorrect statements of results, and to disregard the possibility that the theory might be wrong."
- "An unusually monolithic community, with a strong sense of consensus, whether driven by the evidence or not, and an unusual uniformity of views and open questions."
- "A disregard for and disinterest in the ideas, opinions, and work of experts who are not part of the group, and a preference for talking only with other members of the community."

As proved by the story of string theory, even the most qualified minds in the world aren't immune to frenzy and hype. After all, researchers are people too. The study of string theory was beneficial in many ways, such as the development of new mathematical tools, but its questionable practices are now regarded by many as a dark turn in the history of science; some have even called the theory "fairytale physics" or "fantasy."

Unfortunately, some parts of the artificial intelligence community have adopted the characteristics of the string theory community. Many AI researchers and commentators strongly believe that we're one step away from building computers that are as smart as humans at every task, and they interpret any success in a highly optimistic way, while disregarding evidence to the contrary. If AI fails, they blame it on some practical issue, such as the amount of data, and suggest a patch, without considering that maybe machine learning isn't a sure way to create artificial general intelligence.

I gave a draft of this book to a few AI researchers to collect feedback. One of them, after reading the first chapter, said, "The solution is more data. If you have a big AI that has had most of the internet stuffed into it, it may well understand. I suspect GPT-3 already has enough understanding in it." However, he left no comments about the examples of mistakes made by GPT-3 that I shared later in the book.

Another researcher got very upset and only read the first few pages before throwing up his hands. He did leave some comments in the feedback form, including this endorsement: "AI drives buses and makes literary translations." However, that's an overly positive interpretation of reality, as AI does not drive buses outside very limited and clear paths and publishing houses do not use machines to translate literature. He also said, "Data labeling is a non-problem," citing one type of machine learning application that doesn't require manually labeled data. However, manually labeled data is still needed in many if not most other machine learning applications. At the end of the form, after calling himself an "AI researcher at a prestigious university," he wrote, "Your book reads like you've worked for a 'data science' team in a mid-sized company without doing any research."

There is a similar tone in much of the public commentary around AI. For example, an influential AI commentator posted the following survey on LinkedIn:

What is the most impressive problem that AI has solved so far?

A. Fighting hate speech
B. Avoiding fraud
C. Improving agriculture
D. Preventing diseases

The wording of the survey is a bit strange. The list contains tasks on which AI has probably had a positive impact, but they are presented as problems that AI has "solved." The wording of this survey does not invite the audience to entertain—or discuss—the possibility that AI may not have yet solved those problems fully.

AI has been successfully used for many applications for the first time in history, and it's here to stay. However, the dogmatic attitude toward AI has fomented a disproportionately high wave of hype. In this book, I've tried to show you how AI works in a more realistic way and to demystify the mechanisms behind its hype. As a final takeaway, let me answer for you some questions I frequently receive before sharing my predictions and concerns about AI.

Frequently asked questions

AI has been advancing faster and faster in recent years, so we'll surely keep making impressive strides toward all-powerful AI, right?

Not necessarily. It seems that the current best AI methodology, machine learning, won't be enough to reach human-level performance at all tasks. Notably, its performance is disappointing at tasks that require an extensive knowledge of the world, such as detecting whether a road situation is dangerous or translating multi-faceted words. No one knows how to overcome these issues. So, we would need *innovation*—the discovery of a new methodology—to make the next jump forward. But we cannot predict when innovation will happen. And the fact that innovation has happened recently doesn't necessarily mean that the next breakthrough is coming soon.

The situation is similar to our current understanding of nuclear fusion power—it would be a great way to produce electricity, but no one knows how to do that efficiently yet or when we'll figure it out.

But fully autonomous, self-driving cars are already roaming the streets, right?

Not exactly. There are autonomous vehicles, as there have always been (like aircraft autopilots), but these operate in tightly controlled environments. The challenge is to have a car drive in any environment, such as a busy street in, say, London or Bangkok. Currently, self-driving cars operate only in highly controlled or restricted environments, and the few that have tried to navigate city streets freely have been the source of controversial news (such as the autonomous vehicle that got stuck for several minutes, confused by a line of traffic cones). Many leaders in the industry have already acknowledged that their goals were harder to achieve than they initially thought.

With the increasing power of computers and the wide availability of data, we will certainly be able to build all-powerful machine learning models, right?

Building more powerful machine learning models would simply be doing more of the same thing. So, yes, we can create larger and larger models, but that doesn't solve the main issues the field is currently facing. On this topic, AI guru

Yann LeCun recently said, "The category of people that I might tick off is people who say scaling is enough. So, basically, we just use gigantic transformers, we train them on multimodal data that involves, you know, video, text, blah, blah, blah [...] and somehow AI will emerge out of this. They're not wrong, in the sense that that may be a component of a future intelligent system. But I think it's missing essential pieces."[91] One of the most important missing pieces is comprehensive common-sense knowledge about how the world works. Another missing component is the ability to learn in a more effective way, from fewer examples, as humans do. AI will need to be equipped with these "essential pieces," and maybe more, before truly intelligent systems can emerge.

Should I be afraid of AI?

Probably not in the way a lot of people seem to be afraid, worrying about robots gone rogue, machine-led mass extinction, skyrocketing unemployment, etc. But you might need to be concerned about the consequences of humans being overly optimistic and putting too much trust in the capabilities of AI. Current AI makes mistakes that humans would never make, like confusing a toothbrush with a baseball bat. And it can also be easily fooled. For example, we can alter traffic signs in ways that are imperceptible to the human eye but make the computer misunderstand them. Current AI also struggles in new or uncommon situations that were not present in the data it learned from, but the ability to deal with unprecedented situations is paramount for safety. So, the real fear with AI is that overly optimistic people will think it is infallible and try to deploy it in unsafe ways.

But I read a *Nature* paper that said…

Researchers are humans; they have egos and careers to feed, causing them to cherry-pick results and publicize their work with catchy headlines. I've given many examples in this book. A notable one is an article published by *Nature* titled "Mastering the game Go without human knowledge." While the AI didn't learn from a record of humanly played games, the method did involve extensive human knowledge in its design, making that headline's claim a rather big stretch.

What you're saying may apply to mid-sized companies but certainly not to DeepMind or OpenAI, right?

While AI giants are indeed at the forefront of innovation and have reached outstanding milestones, they don't escape the observations made in this book.

Would you pick a human surgeon with 80% success rate or an AI surgeon with 90% success rate?

I cannot answer this question because we shouldn't evaluate surgeons just by counting successes; we should also analyze them qualitatively. What if the 90%-success AI surgeon sometimes makes unexpected mistakes, as AI often does?

Would I trust a 90%-success AI surgeon that has sometimes botched easy surgeries unexpectedly in ways humans wouldn't have?

At the end of the day, our brains are just machines, so all-powerful AI will be possible in principle one day by building a computer that is sophisticated enough, right?

It's not so simple. Whether or not our brain function is equivalent to digital computers has been disputed and remains the source of much debate. Also, although researchers have managed to map out the brain of an entire organism—a tiny worm with 300 neurons—that hasn't allowed them to simulate the worm's behavior as we still don't know how neurons really work. And the theories themselves that explain the workings of the physical world seem to be in desperate need of a big makeover. A lot is yet unknown.

The future

My impression is that AI—in the form of machine learning—will continue to be adopted to help perform tasks that aren't life-critical or highly sensitive. This has been the case so far—AI has been adopted in tasks like recommending products, highlighting questionable grammar, sorting search results, forecasting demand to optimize operations, and so on. These tasks are quite innocuous. In more critical domains, like healthcare, AI has mostly been used as a tool to help human decision-makers. AI is not driving buses through busy streets, translating legal documents, prosecuting defendants in court, deciding to fire the CEO or having the last word in a medical diagnosis.

My prediction is that this will continue to be the case. The people intending to use AI for critical tasks will be highly disappointed. The industry of self-driving cars will not produce fully autonomous cars that can drive anywhere and will refocus their efforts instead on other, less ambitious goals. Automated translation will keep improving but will still sometimes make silly mistakes that will preclude lawyers or publishing houses from using it.

It also seems to me that we're heading toward a period of waning enthusiasm about AI—a mild AI winter. I get the impression that colder times have already come. Just a few days ago, a tech investor told me he had grown tired of hearing start-ups use the word AI as a hook. Another investor told me she'd started to cringe when a start-up's domain name was "something dot ai." And an individual in charge of assessing grant applications mentioned that they'd grown "sensitive" to the terms "machine learning" and "AI," and now they expect applicants who bring them up to explain at length how they'll use those technologies—buzz words alone aren't working as well as they used to.

I'm not sure the extent to which this slowdown will impact the economy, but, as companies have already poured billions into AI projects, it will probably come at a price.

My biggest fear at the moment is that some people may get caught up in the hype and not acknowledge AI's limitations. I fear that they may consider AI infallible and convince everyone else of that belief, and because of that, people may end up using machine learning for critical tasks it is not prepared to perform safely. Maybe they'll manage to have fully autonomous buses roam busy streets. However, while current AI is a good pretender, sooner or later, it ends up making surprisingly silly—and potentially devastating—mistakes.

RESOURCES

If you want to become a machine learning practitioner:

- *ComputingSchool.com:* My own video course on machine learning and other resources for aspiring tech professionals.
- *Neural Networks and Deep Learning* by Michel Nielsen (neuralnetworksanddeeplearning.com): A friendly introduction to deep learning.
- *An Introduction to Statistical Learning* by Gareth James: A comprehensive textbook on machine learning that is neither too deep nor too shallow.

On the power and limits of AI:

- Scott Aaronson's blog (scottaaronson.blog): A quintessential source of information and spicy debate about AI and quantum computing.

- Filip Piekniewski's blog (blog.piekniewski.info): This blog discusses AI at length—especially self-driving cars—and has made some controversial predictions that went viral.
- mybrainsthoughts.com: This anonymous blog discusses artificial general intelligence and analyzes the power of some of the most famous machine learning models.

On consciousness and the mind:

- *The Conscious Mind* by David Chalmers: A friendly introduction to the hard problem of consciousness and how it pertains to the AI debate.
- *Shadows of the Mind* by Roger Penrose: This book defends a controversial viewpoint about AI. Some parts are very friendly (it's worth getting a copy just to read Chapter 1) and others are quite technical (if you're up for the challenge).
- *Conversations on Consciousness* by Susan Blackmore: A useful systematic overview of the viewpoints on consciousness held by many influential thinkers.

REFERENCES

1   Knapton, S. (2022) "AI can 'plug the gaps in the
    brains' of dementia sufferers," *The Telegraph*, 24
    September. Available at: https://www.telegraph.co.uk/
    news/2022/09/24/ai-can-plug-gaps-brains-dementia-
    sufferers/ (Accessed: November 13, 2022).
2   Petroff, A. (2018) "Google CEO: AI is 'more profound
    than electricity or fire'," *CNN Business*, 24 January.
    Available at: https://money.cnn.com/2018/01/24/
    technology/sundar-pichai-google-ai-artificial-
    intelligence/ (Accessed: November 13, 2022).
3   Cuthbertson, A. (2020) "Elon Musk claims AI
    will overtake humans 'in less than five years'," *The
    Independent*, 27 July. Available at: https://www.
    independent.co.uk/tech/elon-musk-artificial-
    intelligence-ai-singularity-a9640196.html (Accessed:
    November 13, 2022).

4   Simon, H.A. (1960) in *The New Science of Management Decision.* Harper & Brothers, p. 38.

5   Crevier, D. (1995) in *AI: The tumultuous history of the search for Artificial Intelligence.* New York, NY: Basic Books, p. 115.

6   Kautz, H.A. (2022) "The third AI summer: AAAI Robert S. Engelmore Memorial lecture," *AI Magazine,* 43(1), pp. 105–125. Available at: https://doi.org/10.1002/aaai.12036.

7   McCorduck, P. (2004) in *Machines Who Think: A personal inquiry into the history and prospects of artificial intelligence.* Natick, Massachusetts: AK Peters, p. 436.

8   Crevier, D. (1995) in *AI: The tumultuous history of the search for Artificial Intelligence.* New York, NY: Basic Books, p. 199.

9   Crevier, D. (1995) in *AI: The tumultuous history of the search for Artificial Intelligence.* New York, NY: Basic Books, p. 210.

10   Olson, P. (2019) "Nearly Half Of All 'AI Startups' Are Cashing In On Hype," *Forbes,* 4 March. Available at: https://www.forbes.com/sites/parmyolson/2019/03/04/nearly-half-of-all-ai-startups-are-cashing-in-on-hype/ (Accessed: November 13, 2022).

11   Solon, O. (2018) "The rise of 'pseudo-AI': how tech firms quietly use humans to do bots' work," *The Guardian,* 6 July. Available at: https://www.theguardian.

com/technology/2018/jul/06/artificial-intelligence-ai-humans-bots-tech-companies (Accessed: November 13, 2022).

12 "Santa Clara Man Charged With Running Bogus Artificial Intelligence Investment Fraud Scheme" (2020) *U.S. Attorney's Office, Northern District of California.* Available at: https://www.justice.gov/usao-ndca/pr/santa-clara-man-charged-running-bogus-artificial-intelligence-investment-fraud-scheme (Accessed: November 13, 2022).

13 Kelnar, D. (2019) "The State of AI 2019: Divergence," *MMC Ventures,* February. Available at: https://mmc.vc/resources/fund-brochures/The-MMC-State-of-AI-2019-Report.pdf (Accessed: November 13, 2022).

14 Holland-Letz, D. et al. (2021) "Mobility's future: An investment reality check." *McKinsey & Company,* 14 April. Available at: https://www.mckinsey.com/industries/automotive-and-assembly/our-insights/mobilitys-future-an-investment-reality-check (Accessed: November 13, 2022).

15 Millward, D. (2022) "Google engineer suspended after saying AI chatbot was sentient," *The Telegraph,* 12 June. Available at: https://www.telegraph.co.uk/news/2022/06/12/google-ai-has-become-sentient-thinks-like-seven-year-old-says/ (Accessed: November 13, 2022).

16 Cook, J. (2014) "ELON MUSK: Robots Could Delete Humans Like Spam," *Business Insider*, 9 October. Available at: https://www.businessinsider.com/elon-musk-robots-could-delete-humans-like-spam-2014-10 (Accessed: November 13, 2022).

17 Silver, D. et al. (2017) "Mastering the game of go without human knowledge," *Nature,* 550(7676), pp. 354–359. Available at: https://doi.org/10.1038/nature24270.

18 Vigen, T. (2015) *Spurious correlations.* New York: Hachette Books.

19 Russell, S.J. (2020) in *Human Compatible: Artificial Intelligence and the Problem of Control.* London: Penguin Books, p. 141.

20 Davidson, T. et al. (2017) "Automated hate speech detection and the problem of offensive language," *Proceedings of the International AAAI Conference on Web and Social Media,* 11(1), pp. 512–515. Available at: https://doi.org/10.1609/icwsm.v11i1.14955.

21 Lefkowitz, M. (2019) "Study finds racial bias in tweets flagged as hate speech." *Cornell Chronicle,* 5 August. Available at: https://news.cornell.edu/stories/2019/08/study-finds-racial-bias-tweets-flagged-hate-speech (Accessed: November 13, 2022).

22 Krizhevsky, A., Sutskever, I. and Hinton, G.E. (2017) "ImageNet classification with deep

convolutional Neural Networks," *Communications of the ACM,* 60(6), pp. 84–90. Available at: https://doi.org/10.1145/3065386.

23 Silver, D. et al. (2017) "Mastering the game of go without human knowledge," *Nature,* 550 (7676), pp. 354–359. Available at: https://doi.org/10.1038/nature24270.

24 Silver, D. et al. (2016) "Mastering the game of go with deep neural networks and Tree Search," *Nature,* 529(7587), pp. 484–489. Available at: https://doi.org/10.1038/nature16961.

25 LeCun, Y. (1989) Generalization and Network Design Strategies. *Technical report CRG-TR-89-4,* University of Toronto.

26 LeCun, Y. et al. (1989) "Handwritten digit recognition with a back-propagation network," *Advances in Neural Information Processing Systems, 2.*

27 LeCun, Y., Bengio, Y. and Hinton, G. (2015) "Deep learning," *Nature,* 521(7553), pp. 436–444. Available at: https://doi.org/10.1038/nature14539.

28 Srivastava, N. et al. (2014) "Dropout: a Simple Way to Prevent Neural Networks from Overfitting." *The Journal of Machine Learning Research,* 15(1), pp. 1929–1958.

29 Kuutti, S. et al. (2021) "A survey of deep learning applications to Autonomous Vehicle Control," *IEEE*

Transactions on Intelligent Transportation Systems, 22(2), pp. 712–733. Available at: https://doi.org/10.1109/tits.2019.2962338.

30 Szegedy, C. et al. (2013) "Intriguing properties of neural networks," *arXiv preprint arXiv:1312.6199.* Available at: https://doi.org/10.48550/arXiv.1312.6199.

31 Athalye, A. et al. (2018) "Synthesizing robust adversarial examples," *Proceedings of the International Conference on Machine Learning,* 80, pp. 284–293.

32 Eykholt, K. et al. (2018) "Robust Physical-World Attacks on Deep Learning Visual Classification," *Proceedings of the IEEE Conference on Computer Vision and Pattern Recognition.* Available at: https://doi.org/10.1109/cvpr.2018.00175.

33 Dehaene, S. (2021) in *How we learn: The new science of education and the brain.* London: Penguin Books, p. 5.

34 Beery, S., Perona, P. and Van Horn, G. (2018) "Recognition in Terra Incognita," *Proceedings of the European Conference on Computer Vision,* pp. 456–473.

35 Dehaene, S. (2021) in *How we learn: The new science of education and the brain.* London: Penguin Books, p. xxii.

36 Dehaene, S. (2021) in *How we learn: The new science of education and the brain.* London: Penguin Books, p. 40.

37 Kaminski, J., Call, J. and Fischer, J. (2004) "Word learning in a domestic dog: Evidence for 'Fast mapping,'" *Science,* 304(5677), pp. 1682–1683. Available at: https://doi.org/10.1126/science.1097859.

38 Baldwin, D.A. (2014) "Understanding the link between joint attention and language," in C. Moore and P.J. Dunham (editors) *Joint Attention: Its origins and role in development.* Psychology Press.

39 Siegfried, T. (2020) "Why some artificial intelligence is smart until it's dumb," *Knowable Magazine*, 27 August. Available at: https://knowablemagazine.org/article/ technology/2020/why-some-artificial-intelligence- smart-until-its-dumb (Accessed: November 13, 2022).

40 Kocijan, V. et al. (2022) "The Defeat of the Winograd Schema Challenge." *arXiv preprint arXiv:2201.02387.* Available at: https://doi.org/10.48550/ arXiv.2201.02387.

41 Thompson, C. (2014) "Computers will be like humans by 2029: Google's Ray Kurzweil," *CNBC*, 11 June. Available at: https://www.cnbc.com/2014/06/11/ computers-will-be-like-humans-by-2029-googles-ray- kurzweil.html (Accessed: November 13, 2022).

42 Musk, E. (2022) "2029 feels like a pivotal year. I'd be surprised if we don't have AGI by then. Hopefully, people on Mars too." *Twitter,* 30 May. Available at: https://twitter.com/elonmusk/ status/1531328534169493506 (Accessed: November 13, 2022).

43 Kurzweil, R. (2018) in *The Singularity is Near: When humans transcend biology.* Richmond: Duckworth, p. 18.

44	Kurzweil, R. (2018) in *The Singularity is Near: When humans transcend biology.* Richmond: Duckworth, p. 9.

45	Bostrom, N. (2017) in *Superintelligence: Paths, dangers, strategies*. Oxford University Press, p. 20.

46	Thompson, C. (2015) "Elon Musk says Tesla's fully autonomous cars will hit the road in 3 years," *Business Insider*, 25 September. Available at: https://www.businessinsider.com/elon-musk-on-teslas-autonomous-cars-2015-9 (Accessed: November 13, 2022).

47	Marshall, A. (2017) "To Save the Most Lives, Deploy (Imperfect) Self-Driving Cars ASAP," *Wired*, 7 November. Available at: https://www.wired.com/story/self-driving-cars-rand-report/ (Accessed: November 13, 2022).

48	Maddox, T. (2018) "How autonomous vehicles could save over 350K lives in the US and millions worldwide," *ZDNET*, 1 February. Available at: https://www.zdnet.com/article/how-autonomous-vehicles-could-save-over-350k-lives-in-the-us-and-millions-worldwide/ (Accessed: November 13, 2022).

49	Hancock, P. (2018) "Are autonomous cars really safer than human drivers?" *World Economic Forum*, 7 February. Available at: https://www.weforum.org/agenda/2018/02/are-autonomous-cars-really-safer-than-human-drivers (Accessed: November 13, 2022).

50	Hawkins, A.J. (2018) "Inside Waymo's strategy to grow the best brains for self-driving cars." *The*

Verge, 9 May. Available at: https://www.theverge. com/2018/5/9/17307156/google-waymo-driverless-cars-deep-learning-neural-net-interview (Accessed: November 13, 2022).

51 Templeton, B. (2021) "Waymo Performs Embarrassingly in Construction Cone Situation," *Forbes,* 14 May. Available at: https://www.forbes.com/ sites/bradtempleton/2021/05/14/waymo-peforms-embarrassingly-in-construction-cone-situation/ (Accessed: November 13, 2022).

52 Coppola, G. and Bergen, M. (2021) "Waymo Is 99% of the Way to Self-Driving Cars. The Last 1% Is the Hardest," *Bloomberg,* 17 August. Available at: https:// www.bloomberg.com/news/articles/2021-08-17/ waymo-s-self-driving-cars-are-99-of-the-way-there-the-last-1-is-the-hardest (Accessed: November 13, 2022).

53 Musk, E. (2021) "[…] Generalized self-driving is a hard problem, as it requires solving a large part of real-world AI. Didn't expect it to be so hard, but the difficulty is obvious in retrospect. […]" *Twitter,* 21 July. Available at: https://twitter.com/elonmusk/ status/1411280212470366213 (Accessed: November 13, 2022).

54 Bateman, T. (2021) "France approves fully autonomous bus for driving on public roads in a European first," *Euronews,* 21 January. Available at: https://www.

euronews.com/next/2021/12/01/france-approves-fully-autonomous-bus-for-driving-on-public-roads-in-a-european-first (Accessed: November 13, 2022).

55   Dym, C.L. (2013) *Engineering design: A project-based introduction.* John Wiley & Sons.

56   Ries, E. (2011) *The lean startup: How constant innovation creates radically successful businesses.* London: Portfolio Penguin.

57   Horowitz, B. (2014) in *The Hard Thing About Hard Things.* Harper Business, p. 183.

58   Buczynski, W., Cuzzolin, F. and Sahakian, B. (2021) "A review of machine learning experiments in equity investment decision-making: Why most published research findings do not live up to their promise in real life," *International Journal of Data Science and Analytics,* 11(3), pp. 221–242. Available at: https://doi.org/10.1007/s41060-021-00245-5.

59   Aaaronson, S. (2014) "My Conversation with 'Eugene Goostman,' the Chatbot that's All Over the News for Allegedly Passing the Turing Test," *Shtetl-Optimized*, 9 June. Available at: https://scottaaronson.blog/?p=1858 (Accessed: November 13, 2022).

60   "Artificial intelligence accurately predicts who will develop dementia in two years" (2021) *University of Exeter,* 16 December. Available at: https://www.exeter.ac.uk/news/research/title_890569_en.html (Accessed: November 13, 2022).

61 James, C. et al. (2021) "Performance of machine learning algorithms for predicting progression to dementia in memory clinic patients," *JAMA Network Open,* 4(12). Available at: https://doi.org/10.1001/ jamanetworkopen.2021.36553.

62 He, K. et al. (2015) "Delving Deep into Rectifiers: Surpassing human-level performance on ImageNet Classification," *Proceedings of the 2015 IEEE International Conference on Computer Vision.* Available at: https://doi.org/10.1109/iccv.2015.123.

63 Cowley, H.P. et al. (2022) "A framework for rigorous evaluation of human performance in human and Machine Learning Comparison Studies," *Scientific Reports,* 12(1). Available at: https://doi.org/10.1038/ s41598-022-08078-3.

64 Tiku, N. (2022) "The Google engineer who thinks the company's AI has come to life," *The Washington Post,* 11 June. Available at: https://www.washingtonpost. com/technology/2022/06/11/google-ai-lamda-blake-lemoine/ (Accessed: November 13, 2022).

65 "What is LaMDA and What Does it Want?" (2022), 11 June. Available at: https://cajundiscordian. medium.com/what-is-lamda-and-what-does-it-want-688632134489 (Accessed: November 13, 2022).

66 Graham, D. (2021) in *An internet in your head: A new paradigm for how the brain works.* New York: Columbia University Press, p. 65.

67   Penrose, R. (1989) in *The Emperor's New Mind: Concerning computers, mind, and the laws in physics.* Oxford University Press, p. 511.

68   Sardi, S. et al. (2017) "New types of experiments reveal that a neuron functions as multiple independent threshold units," *Scientific Reports,* 7(1). Available at: https://doi.org/10.1038/s41598-017-18363-1.

69   Gidon, A. et al. (2020) "Dendritic action potentials and computation in human layer 2/3 cortical neurons," *Science,* 367(6473), pp. 83–87. Available at: https://doi.org/10.1126/science.aax6239.

70   Jabr, F. (2012) "The Connectome Debate: Is Mapping the Mind of a Worm Worth It?" *Scientific American,* 2 October. Available at: https://www.scientificamerican.com/article/c-elegans-connectome/ (Accessed: November 13, 2022).

71   Chalmers, D.J. (1996) *The Conscious Mind: In search of a fundamental theory.* Oxford University Press.

72   Hawkins, J. and Blakeslee, S. (2004) in *On Intelligence.* New York: St. Martin's Press, p. 194.

73   Chalmers, D.J. (1996) "Absent Qualia, Fading Qualia, Dancing Qualia," in *The Conscious Mind: In search of a fundamental theory.* Oxford University Press, pp. 247–275.

74   Hofstadter, D.R. (1981) "A Conversation with Einstein's Brain," in *The mind's I: Fantasies and*

reflections on self and soul. New York: Basic Books, pp. 430–460.

75 Penrose, R. (1989) in *The Emperor's New Mind: Concerning computers, mind, and the laws in physics.* Oxford University Press, p. 28.

76 Aaronson, S. (2016) "The Ghost in the Quantum Turing Machine," in S.B. Cooper and A. Hodges (editors) *The Once and Future Turing: Computing the world.* Cambridge: Cambridge University Press.

77 Chalmers, D.J. (1996) in *The Conscious Mind: In search of a fundamental theory.* Oxford University Press, p. 294.

78 Bostrom, N. (2017) in *Superintelligence: Paths, dangers, strategies.* Oxford University Press, pp. 28–30.

79 Penrose, R. (1989) *The Emperor's New Mind: Concerning computers, mind, and the laws in physics,* Oxford University Press. Penrose, R. (1994) *Shadows of the Mind: A Search for the Missing Science of Consciousness,* Oxford University Press. Penrose, R. et al. (1997) *The Large, the Small, and the Human Mind,* Cambridge University Press.

80 Penrose, R. (1994) in *Shadows of the Mind: A Search for the Missing Science of Consciousness.* Oxford University Press, p. 26.

81 Chalmers, D.J. (1996) in *The Conscious Mind: In search of a fundamental theory.* Oxford University Press, p. 331.

82 Turing, A.M. (1937) "On Computable Numbers,
    with an Application to the Entscheidungsproblem,"
    Proceedings of the London Mathematical Society, s2-42(1),
    pp. 230–265. Available at: https://doi.org/10.1112/
    plms/s2-42.1.230.

83 Robinson, R.M. (1971) "Undecidability and
    Nonperiodicity for Tilings of the Plane," *Inventiones
    Mathematicae,* 12(3), pp. 177–209. Available at: https://
    doi.org/10.1007/bf01418780.

84 Penrose, R. (1994) in *Shadows of the Mind: A Search for
    the Missing Science of Consciousness.* Oxford University
    Press, p. 76.

85 Franzén Torkel (2005) "Chapter 6: Gödel, Minds, and
    Computers," in *Gödel's theorem: An incomplete guide to its
    use and abuse.* Routledge.

86 Maudlin, T. (2019) in *Philosophy of Physics: Quantum
    Theory.* Princeton University Press, p. 5.

87 Talty, S. (2018) "What Will Our Society Look
    Like When Artificial Intelligence Is Everywhere?"
    Smithsonian Magazine, April. Available at: https://www.
    smithsonianmag.com/innovation/artificial-intelligence-
    future-scenarios-180968403/ (Accessed: November 13,
    2022).

88 Kara-Ali, D. (2021) "What will superintelligent AI
    be capable of doing?" *Inside Telecom,* 24 November.
    Available at: https://insidetelecom.com/what-will-

superintelligent-ai-be-capable-of-doing/ (Accessed: November 13, 2022).

89 Russell, S.J. (2020) in *Human Compatible: Artificial Intelligence and the Problem of Control.* London: Penguin Books, p. 149.

90 Smolin, L. (2008) in *The Trouble with Physics: The rise of string theory, the fall of a science and what comes next.* London: Penguin, p. 284.

91 Ray, T. (2022) "Meta's AI guru LeCun: Most of today's AI approaches will never lead to true intelligence," ZDNET, 24 September. Available at: https://www. zdnet.com/article/metas-ai-guru-lecun-most-of-todays-ai-approaches-will-never-lead-to-true-intelligence/ (Accessed: November 13, 2022).

INDEX

A

Aaronson, Scott 125, 145, 155
A/B testing 102
AGI (artificial general intelligence) 85, 161
AlphaGo 43
AlphaZero 58
artificial brains 58, 139, 146
artificial general intelligence. *See* AGI
autonomous cars. *See* self-driving cars

B

Bostrom, Nick 85, 150
brains
  and CNNs 60, 142, 158, 160, 171
  and computation 142, 149
  and consciousness 141, 148
  and neuroscience 136
  and physics 158, 160
  and precision 154
  and randomness 152
  artificial 58, 139, 146
  as templates for AI 150
  copiability 155
  processing power of 134
  simulating 135, 149, 171
  structure 134
  vs. computers 154

C

categorization 36, 45, 59, 127
Chalmers, David 146, 154
ChatGPT 37, 78
CNN (convolutional neural network) 63
computational theory of mind 151
computer programs
  and artificial brains 139, 143
  and categorization 45
  and consciousness 140, 148
  and copiability 154
  and ethics 145

Made in United States
Orlando, FL
15 August 2024